God's Grace Fuels My Passion

WORKBOOK

by

Dr. Maureen Anderson

Published by **The Word for Winners**
P. O. Box 22229
Mesa, AZ 85277
(480) 669-0102

ISBN-10: 1645503518
ISBN-13: 9781645503514

God's Grace Fuels My Passion WORKBOOK
Dr. Maureen Anderson

Graphic Design Artist: Paul Howalt

THE WORD FOR
Winners

Website: **thewordforwinners.com**

You Tube   **MaureenAnderson.TV**

f   **MaureenAnderson**

⊡   **DrMaureenAnderson**

🐦   **MaureenATV**

God's Grace Fuels My Passion
WORKBOOK

Table of Contents

A Picture of Grace
Chapter 1

Point #1 A Picture of Grace

A. _____ **is what Christ has already done. It's the highest power because everything in the Godhead is contained in grace.**

Romans 7:4 (NKJ)
⁴Therefore, my brethren, you also have become dead to the law through the body of Christ, that you may be married to another—to Him Who was raised from the dead, that we should bear fruit to God.

1. We are dead to the _____ or what we do.

2. The law is no more; it's obsolete.

3. We are married to _____.

4. What is invisible in the Kingdom of God has become _____ in the New Covenant.

Ephesians 5:26-27 (TPT)
²⁶to make us holy and pure, cleansing us through the showering of the pure water of the word of God. ²⁷All that He does in us is designed to make us a mature church for His pleasure, until we become a source of praise to Him—glorious and radiant, beautiful and holy, without fault or flaw.

Answers: Grace, law, Christ, visible

Romans 7:6 (AMPC)
⁶But now we are discharged from the law and have terminated all intercourse with it, having died to what once restrained and held us captive. So now we serve not under [obedience to] the old code of written regulations, but [under obedience to the promptings] of the Spirit in newness [of life].

    5.   We are now in a place of honor.

Point #2 The Old Covenant was about what we do, and the New Covenant is about what Christ has done.

A.   **Every spiritual blessing is a love _____ from our wonderful heavenly Father.**

Ephesians 1:3 (TPT)
³Every spiritual blessing in the heavenly realm has already been lavished upon us as a love gift from our wonderful heavenly Father, the Father of our Lord Jesus—all because He sees us wrapped into Christ. This is why we celebrate Him with all our hearts!

    1.   When we are wrapped up in the _____ of Christ, the blessings are now ours.

Ephesians 1:3 (NKJ)
³Blessed be the God and Father of our Lord Jesus Christ, Who has blessed us with every spiritual blessing in the heavenly places in Christ.

    2.   We step into _____ greatness because Christ's life is flowing through us.

    3.   Christ ministers to me under grace.

Answers: gift, works, Christ's

4. Under law, it was my job. Law makes you sin-conscious.

1 Corinthians 15:56 (NIV)
⁵⁶ The sting of death is sin, and the power of sin is the law.

5. Grace makes you _____-conscious.

Titus 2:11-12 (NIV)
¹¹ For the grace of God has appeared that offers salvation to all people. ¹² It teaches us to say "No" to ungodliness and worldly passions, and to live self-controlled, upright and godly lives in this present age.

B. Grace is a mentor, a _____ to teach us.

1. Grace is a free gift that sets us free from the curse because Christ _____ did it.

2. You can't _____ law and grace. We will get back under the curse.

Galatians 1:7 (TPT)
⁷That is a fake "gospel" that is simply not true. There is only one gospel—the gospel of the Messiah! Yet you have allowed those who mix law with grace to confuse you with lies.

Ephesians 1:3 (TPT)
³Every spiritual blessing in the heavenly realm has already been lavished upon us as a love gift from our wonderful heavenly Father, the Father of our Lord Jesus—all because He sees us wrapped into Christ. This is why we celebrate Him with all our hearts!

Answers: Christ, voice, already, mix

Point #3 The Book of Job is Two Covenants, the Old and New.

Galatians 3:10-11 (NIV)

¹⁰For all who rely on the works of the law are under a curse, as it is written: "Cursed is everyone who does not continue to do everything written in the Book of the Law." ¹¹Clearly no one who relies on the law is justified before God, because "the righteous will live by faith."

A.   Job starts out as a picture of someone who is totally committed to the _____ (or what Job does).

1.   He was _____ to be righteous.

2.   Job was depending on his good works.

3.   The law goes to _____.

Job 1:5 (NIV)

⁵When a period of feasting had run its course, Job would make arrangements for them to be purified. Early in the morning he would sacrifice a burnt offering for each of them, thinking, "Perhaps my children have sinned and cursed God in their hearts." This was Job's regular custom.

4.   Job was _____ driven.

1 John 4:18 (NIV)

¹⁸There is no fear in love. But perfect love drives out fear, because fear has to do with punishment. The one who fears is not made perfect in love.

5.   The law becomes _____. Under law, we find ourselves repenting for things we never even did.

Answers: law, "doing," extremes, fear, addictive

Job 3:25 (NKJ)
25 For the thing I greatly feared has come upon me, and what I dreaded has happened to me.

B. **When you're sin conscious, you depend on _____.**
When you're Christ conscious, you depend on _____.

   1.   _____ can't satisfy the law.

Galatians 3:12 (TPT)
12 But keeping the law does not require faith, but self-effort. For the law teaches, "If you practice the principles of law, you must follow all of them."

   2.   Keeping the law does not require faith, but _____-effort.

C. **Job finally realizes he _____, but that he needs a Redeemer.**

   1.   Job stepped out of law – his good works - out of the curse.

   2.   Then he stepped into the New Covenant of Grace, the covenant of _____.

Job 19:25 (NKJ)
25 For I know that my Redeemer lives, and He shall stand at last on the earth.

Point #4 The New Covenant of Grace

Job 42:10, 12a (NKJ)
10 And the LORD restored Job's losses when he prayed for his friends. Indeed the LORD gave Job twice as much as he had before. 12 Now the LORD blessed the latter days of Job more than his beginning...

Answers: you, Christ, We, self, can't, blessings

5

A. Job is _____.

   1. 14,000 Sheep
   2. 6,000 Camels
   3. 1,000 Yoke of Oxen
   4. 1,000 Female Donkeys

Job 42:13, 15-16 (NKJ)
¹³He also had seven sons and three daughters. ¹⁵In all the land were found no women so beautiful as the daughters of Job; and their father gave them an inheritance among their brothers. ¹⁶After this Job lived one hundred and forty years, and saw his children and grandchildren for four generations.

B. The daughters also inherited the blessing.

Point #5 Old Covenant is blessing and curses. New Covenant is blessing and blessing.

A. The New Covenant is total dependence on the _____ **of Christ.**

B. Jesus was full of grace, and He went from blessing to _____.

John 1:16 (NIV84)
¹⁶From the fullness of His grace we have all received one blessing after another.

John 1:16 (CEV)
¹⁶Because of all that the Son is, we have been given one blessing after another.

Answers: restored, works, blessing

C. Grace is an _____. Supernatural energy that propels us ahead.

1 Corinthians 15:10 (NIV)

[10] But by the grace of God I am what I am, and His grace to me was not without effect. No, I worked harder than all of them—yet not I, but the grace of God that was with me.

Ephesians 1:7b-8 (TPT)

[7]...all because of the cascading riches of His grace. [8]This superabundant grace is already powerfully working in us, releasing within us all forms of wisdom and practical understanding.

1. His grace is superabundant!

2. This grace is already powerfully working _____ us.

3. Grace releases all forms of _____ and practical understanding within us.

4. Grace is what Christ has already _____. Grace is the highest power because everything in the Godhead is contained in grace.

Ephesians 3:20 (TPT)

[20] Never doubt God's mighty power to work in you and accomplish all this. He will achieve infinitely more than your greatest request, your most unbelievable dream, and exceed your wildest imagination! He will outdo them all, for His miraculous power constantly energizes you.

Answers: empowerment, in, wisdom, done

Point #6 God set you up to be successful in Him.

Ephesians 1:11 (TPT)
11Through our union with Christ we too have been claimed by God as His own inheritance. Before we were even born, He gave us our destiny; that we would fulfill the plan of God Who always accomplishes every purpose and plan in His heart.

A.   God gave us our destiny _____ we were born.

    1.   God _____ every purpose and plan for us in His heart.

B.   We don't have to be stressed out about our destiny.

Ephesians 1:11b (TPT)
11Before we were even born, He gave us our destiny; that we would fulfill the plan of God Who always accomplishes every purpose and plan in His heart.

    1.   God gave us our _____.

    2.   Every purpose and plan of God for us is accomplished ahead in God's heart.

    3.   It is already accomplished in the _____.

    4.   Let go, and receive the destiny you already have in the invisible.

        a.   _____ the destiny God already accomplished in His heart for you.

        b.   Allow it to flow through you.

Answers: before, accomplishes, destiny, unseen, Embrace

C. _____ go, and _____ the Holy Spirit do His job.

Philippians 1:6 (NIV)
⁶ being confident of this, that He Who began a good work in you will carry it on to completion until the day of Christ Jesus.

being confident – means fully knowing, trusting, and resting

    1.   Allow God to be the boss. Relax and _____.

        a.   We get stressed out in our own _____ effort of doing, doing, doing.

    2.   Trust it's already done in Him.

        a.   Never, ever have the slightest doubt in your mind that God will do what He has <u>already done</u> for you.

D.   You were not made by a _____ cutter.

    1.   You are a custom-made, unique, one-of-a-kind destiny-planned-from-the-beginning-of-time child of God!

Philippians 2:13 (NIV)
¹³ for it is <u>God Who works</u> in you to will and to act in order to fulfill His good purpose.

    2.   It is *<u>God Who works</u>* **– It is not your** _____.

Answers: Let, let, receive, human, cookie, strength

Philippians 2:13 (AMP)
¹³For it is [not your strength, but it is] God Who is effectively at work in you, both to will and to work [that is, strengthening, energizing, and creating in you the longing and the ability to fulfill your purpose] for His good pleasure.

    3.   God has already _____ His purpose for you in the unseen, and it cannot fail in Him.

    4.   Grace means that Christ did it all.

       a.   We just walk in _____ works.

Philippians 2:13 (TPT)
¹³ God will continually revitalize you, implanting within you the passion to do what pleases Him.

1 Thessalonians 5:24 (NIV)
²⁴ The One who calls you is <u>faithful</u>, and He will do it.

<u>faithful</u> – means trustworthy

E.   God called you, and He is faithful to work His _____ purpose through you. Why? Because He already did it!

    1.   Our part is to _____, believe, receive, and let it flow through us.

F.   Jesus shows us the way.

John 5:30a (NIV)
³⁰By Myself I can do _____.

Answers: fulfilled, His, His, surrender, nothing

1. It's Father God, in Jesus, flowing _____ Him and doing the works.

John 8:28 (NIV)
28 So Jesus said, "When you have lifted up the Son of Man, then you will know that I am He and that I do nothing on My own but speak just what the Father has taught Me.

John 7:16 (NIV)
16 Jesus answered, "My teaching is not My own. It comes from the One Who sent Me."

2. Jesus is giving us a picture of when He walked this earth. That it wasn't Him doing the works, but Father God flowing _____ Him.

John 15:4-5 (NIV)
4 Remain in Me, as I also remain in you. No branch can bear fruit by itself; it must remain in the vine. Neither can you bear fruit unless you remain in Me. 5 I am the vine; you are the branches. If you remain in Me and I in you, you will bear much fruit; apart from Me you can do nothing.

3. It's not you, but it's _____ _____ you.

G. Let _____ flow through you.

1. We can get ourselves stressed out with our _____ thinking. "I have to do, do, do!"

2. _____ thinking is Jesus did, did, did!

Answers: through, through, Me, in, grace, legalistic, Grace

11

We are the branch.
The Vine (Jesus) flows through the branch to produce fruit.

THIS IS THE PICTURE
OF THE GRACE LIFE

Holy Spirit
Revealer of Our Destiny
Chapter 2

Point #1 Grace binds us to the blessings.

A.   The grace of God (what Christ has done) binds us to the
      _____ of God that are working for us.

B.   The law (what _____ do) binds us to the curse.

   1.   We are now born-again believers.

1 Corinthians 15:56 (NKJ)   ⌐empowering the sin
*56 The sting of death is sin, and the **strength** of sin is the law.*

1 Corinthians 15:56 (NIV)
56 ...the power of sin is the law.

C.   Grace has the power and ability to keep us from sinning
      because it's _____.

   1.   It's what Christ has already done.

Titus 2:11-12 (NIV)
*11 For the grace of God has appeared that offers salvation to all people.
12 It teaches us to say "No" to ungodliness and worldly passions, and
to live self-controlled, upright and godly lives in this present age.*

   2.   Under the law, we are _____ driven, not faith driven.
         Faith driven is focusing on what Christ has done.

Answers: blessings, we, supernatural, fear

13

3.   We are now in Christ. Grace _____ in us.

   a.   Grace is the _____ of God, that voice of God that teaches and mentors us, gives us the power to say "no" to sin.

   b.   Grace is a _____ of God that teaches us to have an upright, self-controlled, godly life.

   c.   We love grace's power and ability that is working in us to set us up for success.

   d.   Grace brings us into God's love, passion, life, and life more abundant → divine _____ of God.

Galatians 3:18 (TPT)

[18]*The law, then, doesn't supersede the promise since the royal proclamation was given before the law. If that were the case, it would have nullified what God said to Abraham. We receive all the promises because of the Promised One—not because we keep the law.*

4.   All the promises are deeded to us because of _____.

   a.   The promises where not deeded to us because of the law or religious tactics.

Point #2 Christ paid our penalty in full.

A.   Understand, the promises are ours because of what Christ _____ done.

   1.   He _____ our penalty in full.

Answers: abides, power, force, nature, Jesus, has, paid

14

a. Jesus took all our sins to the cross.

b. Jesus totally set us _____.

2. Jesus took all our sins to the cross so we could have eternal life.

3. Jesus took all our sins to the cross so we could live in all the _____ of God.

a. Not because _____ keep the law.

b. We don't receive the blessings by keeping the law.

c. It's not by _____ effort, but it's in His life, His works.

Acts 17:28a (NIV)
28 For in Him we live and move and have our being.

1 John 4:17 (NKJ)
17...as He is, so are we in this world.

John 1:16 (NIV84)
16From the fullness of His grace we have all received one blessing after another.

4. Jesus states that in grace we just go from blessing to _____ in life.

Answers: free, blessings, we, human, blessing

15

Point #3 Enter God's Rest

John 5:30a (NIV)

30By myself I can do nothing…

John 15:5 (NIV)

5I am the vine; you are the branches. If you remain in Me and I in you, you will bear much fruit; apart from Me you can do nothing.

A. In the Kingdom of God, we must realize we _____ apart from Him, but Jesus has already done it all for us.

1. It's _____ in the Kingdom.

2. It's Jesus Who is going to flow through you by the Holy Spirit to bear much fruit.

3. Let Jesus and the Word flow _____ you!

B. In the Covenant of Grace, enter the _____ of God.

1. _____ it's already done.

2. _____ it.

3. Let it flow through you.

Acts 2:22 (NIV)

22 "Fellow Israelites, listen to this: Jesus of Nazareth was a man accredited by God to you by miracles, wonders and signs, which God did among you through Him, as you yourselves know.

Answers: can't, finished, through, rest, Believe, Receive

16

Point #4 Take the invisible in God's heart, and make it visible in your life.

A.   We are born-again of the _____ seed.

James 1:21b (NKJ)
21 ...receive with meekness the implanted Word, which is able to save your soul.

3 John 1:2 (NKJ)
2 Beloved, I pray that you may prosper in all things and be in health, just as your soul prospers.

    1.   We are _____ in Christ, but then we get into works or law.

    2.   Return to your first love.

1 Peter 1:23 (NKJ)
23 having been born again, not of corruptible seed but incorruptible, through the Word of God which lives and abides forever.

Matthew 11:28-30 (NIV)
28 Come to Me, all you who are weary and burdened, and I will give you rest. 29 Take My yoke upon you and learn from Me, for I am gentle and humble in heart, and you will find rest for your souls. 30 For My yoke is easy and My burden is light.

B.   Take _____ yoke upon you.

Answers: incorruptible, complete, His

C.   Since I have come into the revelation of the Covenant of Grace, my prayer for the children's church NOW through the Holy Spirit is this:

Father God,
Before the foundation of time, You already picked the team. You put destiny in those You have already chosen to work in children's church, and I believe it. I receive them from wherever they live on this earth, only those You have chosen for divine connection for your purpose.   **In Jesus Name   Amen**

GOD HAS ALREADY PROVIDED

1.   And _____ did it! Yay!

2.   Make a _____ on the Word of God.

Luke 10:2 (NIV)
2He told them, "The harvest is plentiful, but the workers are few. Ask the Lord of the harvest, therefore, to send out workers into His harvest field."

3.   When we pray like this for others, the Holy Spirit begins to _____ on them through dreams, visions, thoughts, desires, and passion.

a.   The _____ of the Holy Spirit are released to flow to bring them into the children's ministry.

Colossians 3:2 (TPT)
2Yes, feast on all the treasures of the heavenly realm and fill your thoughts with heavenly realities, and not with the distractions of the natural realm.

Answers: God,   demand,   move,   gifts

4. _____ on all the treasures of the heavenly realm.

5. Fill your thoughts with heavenly realities.

6. We are not to be _____ by the natural realm.

Ephesians 1:3 (TPT)

³Every spiritual blessing in the heavenly realm has already been lavished upon us as a love gift from our wonderful heavenly Father, the Father of our Lord Jesus—all because He sees us wrapped into Christ. This is why we celebrate Him with all our hearts!

7. Every spiritual blessing is in the _____.

8. Now your part is to embrace it as already _____ and receive it.

Galatians 1:12 (TPT)

¹²No one taught me this revelation, for it was given to me directly by the unveiling of Jesus the Anointed One.

D. Paul experienced the _____ revelation of grace.

Galatians 1:15-16 (TPT)

¹⁵But then God called me by His grace; and in love, He chose me from my birth to be His. ¹⁶God's grace unveiled His Son in me so that I would proclaim Him to the non-Jewish people of the world. After I had this encounter I kept it a secret for some time, sharing it with no one.

Answers: Feast, distracted, unseen, done, full

1. God put destiny _____ us, and set us up to be successful.

    a. He already did it!

    b. He already _____ us successful in Christ.

2. The Holy Spirit is the _____ of your destiny.

    a. It's the Holy Spirit's part to reveal it to you.

    b. Your part is to _____ to the plan, receive it, and let Christ flow through you.

Romans 8:27 (TPT)
[27]God, the searcher of the heart, knows fully our longings, yet He also understands the desires of the Spirit, because the Holy Spirit passionately pleads before God for us, His holy ones, in perfect harmony with God's plan and our destiny.

Answers: in, made, Revealer, surrender

God's Timing is Now
Chapter 3

Point #1 When we surrender to grace, we effortlessly fulfill the plan God has for us.

A. _____ **to grace with great joy!**

    1.   We surrender to grace with great joy because grace works through us to do destiny that's already done in the _____.

    2.   Surrendered to grace, we love, forgive, and walk by faith.

Ephesians 3:20 (NKJ)
[20] Now to Him Who is able to do exceedingly abundantly above all that we ask or think, according to the power that works in us.

    3.   The Word of God instructs us to never doubt the _____ in grace.

Ephesians 3:20 (TPT)
[20] Never doubt God's might power to work in you and accomplish all this. He will achieve infinitely more that your greatest request, your most unbelievable dream, and exceed your wildest imagination! He will outdo them all, for His miraculous power constantly energizes you.

B. _____ **opens the way to enter into the life of grace.**

Romans 5:2 (NKJ)
[2] through Whom also we have access by faith into this grace in which we stand, and rejoice in hope of the glory of God.

Answers: Surrender, unseen, energy, Faith

1. Faith is in the _____.

2. When we step into the unseen, there is no time.

Hebrews 11:1 (NKJ)
¹¹Now faith is the substance of things hoped for, the evidence of things not seen.

3. We enter into faith that is always now. Hope is in the _____.

    a. In faith we see it done now. We see it _____ now.

Point #2 Don't Say, "It's Not God's Time."

2 Corinthians 6:2 (NKJ)
²For He says: "In an acceptable time I have heard you, and in the day of salvation I have helped you." Behold, now is the accepted time; behold, now is the day of salvation.

John 4:35 (NKJ)
³⁵Do you not say, "There are still four months and then comes the harvest?" Behold, I say to you, lift up your eyes and look at the fields, for they are already white for harvest!

A.   In rebuilding the temple – God said to Ezra, "It's_____!"

Ezra 1:1-2 (NKJ)
¹Now in the first year of Cyrus king of Persia, that the word of the LORD by the mouth of Jeremiah might be, fulfilled the LORD stirred up the

Answers: now, future, finished, now

22

Ezra 1:1-2 (NKJ) Continued

spirit of Cyrus king of Persia, so that he made a proclamation throughout all his kingdom, and also put it in writing, saying, ² "Thus says Cyrus king of Persia: 'All the kingdoms of the earth the LORD God of heaven has given me. And He has commanded me to build Him a house at Jerusalem which is in Judah'"

Book of Ezra - During Ezra's time, the Jewish exiles headed to Jerusalem to rebuild the temple. God _____ them to rebuild it. It was time. They worked hard in laying the foundation. They were so excited that they had an over-the-top celebration, and right after the celebration, the enemy came.

1. The _____ came at them with all force.

Ezra 4:4-5 (NKJ)

⁴Then the people of the land tried to discourage the people of Judah. They troubled them in building, ⁵and hired counselors against them to frustrate their purpose all the days of Cyrus King of Persia, even until the reign of Darius King of Persia.

Ezra 4:23 (NKJ)

²³ ...and by force of arms made them cease.

The enemy came against them with full force. They were so overwhelmed that they said, "It's just not the _____ of God to go on." They left the new foundation they had just laid untouched for 14 years. After 14 years, God had had enough! They had been sent to Jerusalem by God to build the temple.

When the storm came at Ezra and his men they _____ for 14 years. Of course, we have never done that. Quit and say, "It's just not

Answers: called, enemy, timing, quit

23

God's timing." But they quit! They had legalistic _____, "It's in the future." Faith thinking is, "It's now! I already have it!"

2. They had difficulties that seemed so overwhelming. (Jesus said, "We are going to the other side." Then the _____ came.)

3. They stopped for 14 years after the foundation was laid. (All authority has been given to us.)

B. They needed a paradigm shift from legalistic thinking to _____ thinking → It's now!

1. "In the future" or "not _____ timing" is law thinking. It's hoping. Hope is in the future.

2. Faith thinking is now, already _____.

Hebrews 11:1 (NKJ) (Title Deed)
¹¹Now faith is the substance of things hoped for, the evidence of things not seen. **(proof of things)**

Ezekiel 12:22 (NKJ)
²² Son of man, what is this proverb **(this saying)** *that you people have about the land of Israel, which says, "The days are <u>prolonged</u>, and every vision fails?"*

3. The word **prolonged** in Hebrew is <Arak>

a. **Prolonged** means _____, delayed or postponed. <This is talking about the temple.>

b. They were saying, "Every **vision** <chazon> _____." "Every Word of God, **fails** <abad>, is destroyed, given up as lost, and vanished." "It's been 14 years!"

c. They were saying, "No _____ ever comes to anything."

Ezekiel 12:23 (NKJ)

²³*Tell them therefore, thus says the Lord GOD: "I will lay this proverb (this saying) to rest, and they shall no more use it as a proverb in Israel." But say to them, "The days are at hand, and the fulfillment of every vision."*

4. God was saying, "_____ say, 'God postpones, God gives setbacks.'" This is a lie.

5. It's up to us to _____ agree with any more setbacks in our lives.

6. Redeem the time for the days are evil. (Eph. 5:16)

2 Corinthians 6:2 (NKJ)

²*For He says: "In an acceptable time I have heard you, and in the day of salvation I have helped you." Behold, now is the accepted time; behold, now is the day of salvation.*

7. God says, "The time is _____ - TO-DAY!"

Answers: fails, vision, Don't, NOT, now

Ezekiel 12:25 (NKJ)

^{25}*"For I am the LORD. I speak, and the word which I speak will come to pass; it will no more be* <u>postponed</u>; *for in your days, O rebellious house, I will say the word and perform it," says the Lord GOD.*

   8.   God says, "It will no more be postponed." It will no more be _____ or put off.

   9.   God has _____ performed His Word now.

   10. God speaks and does NOW, because it is already done.

John 4:35 (NKJ) (Jesus says:)

^{35}*Do you not say, "There are still four months and then comes the harvest?" Behold, I say to you, "Lift up your eyes and look at the fields, for they are already white for harvest!"*

   11. Don't _____, "It's many days from now…, that time is far off."

C.   Enter into the rest of God. Jesus said, "It is finished!"

Hebrews 4:1-3 (NKJ)

^{1}*Therefore, since a promise remains of entering His rest, let us fear lest any of you seem to have come short of it. ^{2}For indeed the gospel was preached to us as well as to them; but the word which they heard did not profit them, not being mixed with faith in those who heard it. ^{3}For we who have believed do enter that rest, as He has said: So I swore in My wrath, "They shall not enter My rest," although the works were finished from the foundation of the world.*

Answers: delayed, already, say

Ezekiel 12:28 (NKJ)

28Therefore say to them, "Thus says the Lord GOD: 'None of My words will be postponed any more, but the word which I speak will be done,' says the Lord GOD."

1.   None of God's words are _____.

2.   The Word God speaks is already _____.

2 Corinthians 4:18 (NKJ)

18 while we do not look at the things which are seen, but at the things which are not seen. For the things which are seen are temporary, but the things which are not seen are eternal.

Answers: postponed, done

27

Show Us the Father
Chapter 4

Point #1 The Theme is the Gospel of Grace in the Book of Galatians

A. **Grace is all that God has_____ done for us to put us in a life of blessing and totally free us from the curse because of the sacrifice of Jesus on the cross, His death, burial and resurrection.**

   1. Grace requires no _____ from us.
      Dr. Maureen:
      a. "Under the Old Covenant thinking, 'I can do it,' I was always disappointed. Things turned out way <u>beneath</u> my expectation."

      b. "After receiving the new Covenant of Grace in my heart, it's now _____ doing it through me. Now things turn out way <u>beyond</u> my expectation."

   2. In grace, we are required to just relax (submit), receive and let it flow through us from the Lord.

      a. No effort or work, on our part, is necessary. Just _____ the promises.

      b. Why? Because grace revitalizes you, _____ within you the passion to accomplish what pleases Him.

Answers: freely, help, Christ, receive, implanting

Philippians 2:13 (TPT)

¹³*God will continually revitalize you, implanting within you the passion to do what pleases Him.*

  c. God's grace fuels my passion. It continually
     _____ me and implants that passion into me.

Ephesians 3:9 (TPT)

⁹*My passion is to enlighten every person to this divine mystery.*

  d. The grace of God constantly _____ you.

Ephesians 3:20 (TPT)

²⁰*Never doubt God's mighty power to work in you and accomplish all this. He will achieve infinitely more than your greatest request, your most unbelievable dream, and exceed your wildest imagination! He will outdo them all, for His miraculous power constantly energizes you.*

Ephesians 3:8 (TPT)

⁸ *Grace alone empowers me.*

  3. Because of God's _____, we can experience all
    that God has for us. It is now ours.

Galatians 4:7 (NKJ)

⁷*Therefore you are no longer a slave but a son, and if a son, then an heir of God through Christ.*

Galatians 3:18

¹⁸*The law, then, doesn't supersede the promise since the royal proclamation was given before the law. If that were the case, it would have nullified what God said to Abraham. We receive all the promises because of the Promised One—not because we keep the law!*

Answers: revitalizes, energizes, grace

4. We just need to _____.

Ephesians 1:3 (TPT)
³Every spiritual blessing in the heavenly realm has already been lavished upon us as a love gift from our wonderful heavenly Father, the Father of our Lord Jesus—all because He sees us wrapped into Christ. This is why we celebrate Him with all our hearts!

B. Paul's prayer over the Galatians and over _____!

Galatians 1:3 (TPT)
³I pray over you a release of the <u>blessings</u> of God's undeserved kindness and total well-being that flows from our Father-God and from the Lord Jesus.

    1. The word *blessings* in this scripture means a release of wealth, health, peace, love, being highly favored, joy, and so much more! It's life and life more _____.

John 1:14 (NIV)
¹⁴The Word became flesh and made His dwelling among us. We have seen His glory, the glory of the One and only Son, Who came from the Father full of grace and truth.

John 1:16 (NIV84)
¹⁶From the fullness of His grace we have all received one blessing after another.

John 1:17 (NKJ)
¹⁷For the law was given through Moses, but grace and truth came through Jesus Christ.

Answers: receive, us, abundant

30

    a.   Moses brought the Law, the Old Covenant, what
          _____ do.

    b.   Jesus brought grace and truth. The New Covenant,
          what He has already done. We are to be _____.

2.   Jesus <u>gave</u> _____ for us.

Galatians 1:4 (TPT)

[4]He's the Anointed Messiah Who offered Himself as the sacrifice for our sins! He has taken us out of this evil world system and set us free through our salvation, just as God desired.

    a.   This is the message of the Gospel, Jesus' death, burial
          and resurrection, salvation, for us just as God desired.

    b.   God so loved that He _____.

John 3:16 (NKJ)

[16]For God so loved the world that He gave His only begotten Son…

    c.   The false teachers were trying to entice Christians to
          get back _____ the law.

3.   They were leaving the grace of God and entering into the bondage of the Mosaic Law, from liberty to _____.

4.   Paul is overwhelmed that they have started in this negative direction, going after "another gospel".

5.   He is bewildered at their _____. They had the opportunity of sitting under his ministry not just once, but twice.

Answers: we, receivers, all, gave, under, legalism, instability

6. He is shocked by the idea that anyone could _____ or pervert the Gospel.

7. They had not bothered to consult Paul, their spiritual father, and were, in effect, following a stranger's teachings. It was like they were eating candy, polluted candy at that!

   a. I can _____ it.

   b. I can _____ it.

Galatians 1:6-7 (TPT)

6I am shocked over how quickly you have strayed away from the Anointed One Who called you to Himself by His loving mercy. I'm frankly astounded that you now embrace a distorted gospel! 7That is a fake "gospel" that is simply not true. There is only one gospel—the gospel of the Messiah! Yet you have allowed those who mingle law with grace to confuse you with lies.

Galatians 3:18 (NIV)

18For if the inheritance depends on the law, then it no longer depends on the promise; but God in His grace gave it to Abraham through a promise.

Galatians 2:21 (NIV)

21I do not set aside the grace of God, for if righteousness could be gained through the law, Christ died for nothing!

Galatians 5:4 (NIV)

4You who are trying to be justified by the law have been alienated from Christ; you have fallen away from grace.

Answers: twist, do, earn

Romans 7:6 (AMPC)
⁶*But now we are discharged from the Law and have terminated all intercourse with it, having died to what once restrained and held us captive. So now we serve not under [obedience to] the old code of written regulations, but [under obedience to the promptings] of the Spirit in newness [of life].*

C. When you see Jesus, you see the _____.

John 14:9 (NIV)
⁹*Jesus answered: "Don't you know me, Philip, even after I have been among you such a long time? Anyone who has seen Me has seen the Father. How can you say, 'Show us the Father'?"*

Colossians 1:15 (NKJ)
¹⁵*He* **(Jesus)** *is the image of the invisible God, the firstborn over all creation.*

　　1. Jesus extends _____ to the woman at the well.

John 4:6-21 (NKJ)
⁶*Now Jacob's well was there. Jesus therefore, being wearied from His journey, sat thus by the well. It was about the sixth hour.* ⁷*A woman of Samaria came to draw water. Jesus said to her,*
"Give Me a drink."
⁸*For His disciples had gone away into the city to buy food.* ⁹*Then the woman of Samaria said to Him,*
"How is it that You, being a Jew, ask a drink from me, a Samaritan woman? For Jews have no dealings with Samaritans."
¹⁰*Jesus answered and said to her,*

Answers: Father, grace

33

"If you knew the gift of God, and Who it is Who says to you, 'Give Me a drink,' you would have asked Him, and He would have given you living water."

[11]*The woman said to Him,*

"Sir, You have nothing to draw with, and the well is deep. Where then do You get that living water? [12]Are You greater than our father Jacob, who gave us the well, and drank from it himself, as well as his sons and his livestock?"

[13]*Jesus answered and said to her,*

"Whoever drinks of this water will thirst again, [14]but whoever drinks of the water that I shall give him will never thirst. But the water that I shall give him will become in him a fountain of water springing up into everlasting life."

[15]*The woman said to Him,*

"Sir, give me this water, that I may not thirst, nor come here to draw."

[16]*Jesus said to her,*

"Go, call your husband, and come here."

[17]*The woman answered and said,*

"I have no husband."

Jesus said to her,

"You have well said, 'I have no husband,' [18]for you have had five husbands, and the one whom you now have is not your husband; in that you spoke truly."

[19]*The woman said to Him,*

"Sir, I perceive that You are a prophet. [20]Our fathers worshiped on this mountain, and you Jews say that in Jerusalem is the place where one ought to worship."

[21]*Jesus said to her,*

"Woman, believe Me, the hour is coming when you will neither on this mountain, nor in Jerusalem, worship the Father."

2.   Jesus extends grace to the woman caught in _____.

Answer: adultery

John 8:4-5 (NIV)

⁴and said to Jesus, "Teacher, this woman was caught in the act of adultery. ⁵In the Law Moses commanded us to stone such women. Now what do You say?"

John 8:10-11 (NIV)

¹⁰Jesus straightened up and asked her, "Woman, where are they? Has no one condemned you?" ¹¹"No one, sir," she said. "Then neither do I condemn you," Jesus declared. "Go now and leave your life of sin."

3.   Jesus extends grace to the woman who lived a sinful life and washed His feet with her _____. (Luke 7:37)

Luke 7:39 (NIV)

³⁹When the Pharisee who had invited him saw this, he said to himself, "If this man were a prophet, he would know who is touching him and what kind of woman she is—that she is a sinner."

Luke 7:44-50 (NKJ)

⁴⁴Then He turned to the woman and said to Simon, "Do you see this woman? I entered your house; you gave Me no water for My feet, but she has washed My feet with her tears and wiped them with the hair of her head. ⁴⁵You gave Me no kiss, but this woman has not ceased to kiss My feet since the time I came in. ⁴⁶You did not anoint My head with oil, but this woman has anointed My feet with fragrant oil. ⁴⁷Therefore I say to you, her sins, which are many, are forgiven for she loved much. But to whom little is forgiven, the same loves little." ⁴⁸Then He said to her, "Your sins are forgiven." ⁴⁹And those who sat at the table with Him began to say to themselves, "Who is this who even forgives sins?" ⁵⁰Then He said to the woman, "Your faith has saved you. Go in peace."

Answer: tears

<Your sins are forgiven and your faith has saved you.>

4. Jesus was full of compassion to _____ people and set them free. (Isaiah 61 NKJ)

5. Jesus was _____ like us in every way. (Hebrews 2:17-18 NKJ)

Hebrews 1:3 (NIV)

³The Son is the radiance of God's glory **(power and character)** *and the exact representation of His being, sustaining all things by His powerful Word.*

6. Jesus is the exact representation of a Father God Who is _____ of mercy, compassion, unconditional love, favor, value, grace, and joy for us.

    a. A Father Who _____ Rahab, the prostitute, and Jacob's daughter-in-law.

    b. A Father Who understands our prisons.

    c. A Father Who understands addictions, our helpless-ness, and He _____.

    d. A Father Who understands wrong decisions in life and makes a way of _____.

D. The right image of God is our _____ Father.

1. A Father Who so_____ the world, He gave it all.

Answers: heal, made, full, saved, cares, escape, loving, loved

36

Luke 19:1-6 (NIV)

¹*Jesus entered Jericho and was passing through.* ²*A man was there by the name of Zacchaeus; he was a chief tax collector and was wealthy.* ³*He wanted to see who Jesus was, but because he was short he could not see over the crowd.* ⁴*So he ran ahead and climbed a sycamore-fig tree to see him, since Jesus was coming that way.* ⁵*When Jesus reached the spot, He looked up and said to him, "Zacchaeus, come down immediately. I must stay at your house today."* ⁶*So he came down at once and welcomed him gladly.*

Ephesians 1:3 (TPT)

³*Every spiritual blessing in the heavenly realm has already been lavished upon us as a love gift from our wonderful heavenly Father, the Father of our Lord Jesus—all because He sees us wrapped into Christ. This is why we celebrate Him with all our hearts!*

E.   It is _____ that we have the right image of Father God within us.

    1.   The right image will make it so we are able to trust Father God with our _____ heart so that we make the right choices in life.

        And this never changes.

        This is _____.

Answers: vital,   whole,   grace

Grace is an Energy,
a Force, a Power
Chapter 5

Point #1 We need to get free of our religious, legalistic behaviors and belief systems about our Father God that harm our walk and the way we behave.

Ephesians 1:3 (TPT)
³Every spiritual blessing in the heavenly realm has already been lavished upon us as a love gift from our wonderful heavenly Father, the Father of our Lord Jesus—all because He sees us wrapped into Christ. This is why we celebrate Him with all our hearts!

Jesus portrayed the Father's _____ to us.

Religion and law _____ the character of Father God. It paints a false image of God, not the loving caring, giving, true image of Father God. It paints a false image of Father God as a heavy task master, a policeman or a stern boss.

A.   A miracle for Jairus' daughter.

Mark 5:22-24 (NIV)
²²Then one of the synagogue leaders, named Jairus, came, and when he saw Jesus, he fell at His feet. ²³He pleaded earnestly with Him, "My little daughter is dying. Please come and put Your hands on her so that she will be healed and live." ²⁴So Jesus went with him. A large crowd followed and pressed around Him.

B.   Jesus _____ the dead daughter of Jairus.

Answers: character, attack, raises

Mark 5:35-42 (NIV)

35While Jesus was still speaking, some people came from the house of Jairus, the synagogue leader.

"Your daughter is dead," they said.

"Why bother the teacher anymore?"

36Overhearing what they said, Jesus told him,

"Don't be afraid; just believe."

37He did not let anyone follow Him except Peter, James and John the brother of James. 38When they came to the home of the synagogue leader, Jesus saw a commotion, with people crying and wailing loudly. 39He went in and said to them,

"Why all this commotion and wailing? The child is not dead but asleep."

40But they laughed at Him. After He put them all out, He took the child's father and mother and the disciples who were with Him and went in where the child was. 41He took her by the hand and said to her, "Talitha koum!" (which means "Little girl, I say to you, get up!"). 42Immediately the girl stood up and began to walk around (she was twelve years old). At this they were completely astonished.

Point #2 Do we see Father God as the Heavy Task Master – Who has only conditional love and blessings for us?

A. **Do I believe God will _____ me, reward me and be pleased with me based on my service to Him? Am I an overachiever?**

    1.   Will He bless me through my religious _____?

    2.   Jesus said the works of the Father are to <u>believe</u> on Whom He sent.

B. **The Word of God is the _____.**

Answers: love, performance, seed

Luke 8:11 (NIV)

[1]*"This is the meaning of the parable: The seed is the Word of God.*

Genesis 8:22 (NIV)

[22]*As long as the earth endures, seedtime and harvest, cold and heat, summer and winter, day and night will never cease.*

    1.   Seed _____ indicates two separate words.

        a.   Seed is _____ the Word of God.

        b.   Time is where the _____ is.

1 Timothy 6:12 (NIV)

[12]*Fight the good fight of the faith. Take hold of the eternal life to which you were called when you made your good confession in the presence of many witnesses.*

Mark 4:15, 17 (NIV)

[15]*Some people are like seed along the path, where the Word is sown. As soon as they hear it, Satan comes and takes away the Word that was sown in them.* [17]*But since they have no root, they last only a short time. When trouble or persecution comes because of the Word they quickly fall away.*

    2.   The enemy comes to _____ the Word of God or persecute us because of it.

Ephesians 3:20 (NIV)

[20]*Now to Him Who is able to do immeasurably more than all we ask or imagine according to His power that is at work within us.*

Answers: time, planting, battle, steal

Matthew 11:29-30 (NIV)
^{29}*Take My yoke* **(grace)** *upon you and learn from Me, for I am gentle and humble in heart, and you will find rest for your souls.* ^{30}*For My yoke is easy and My burden is light."*

    3.   Make every effort to enter My_____.

Hebrew 4:10 (NKJ)
^{10}*For he who has entered His rest has himself also ceased from his works as God did from His.*

Ephesians 2:10 (NKJ)
^{10}*For we are His workmanship, created in Christ Jesus for good works, which God prepared beforehand that we should walk in them.*

Philippians 2:13 (TPT)
^{13}*God will continually revitalize you, implanting within you the passion to do what pleases Him.*

Philippians 3:12b-13a (TPT)
^{12}*...I run with passion into His abundance* **(everything in the Kingdom)** *so that I may reach the purpose that Jesus Christ has called me to fulfill and wants me to discover.* ^{13}*I don't depend on my own strength to accomplish this...*

Ephesians 1:2 (TPT)
^{2}*I'm writing this letter to all the devoted believers who have been made holy by being one with Jesus, the Anointed One. May God Himself, the heavenly Father of our Lord Jesus Christ, release grace over you and impart total well-being into your lives.*

Answers: rest

Ephesians 1:6 (TPT)
⁶—for the same love He has for His Beloved One, Jesus, He has for us. And this unfolding plan brings Him great pleasure!

Ephesians 3:9 (TPT)
⁹My passion is to enlighten every person to this divine mystery. It was hidden for ages past until now, and kept a secret in the heart of God, the Creator of all.

    a.   It's resting in Father God's sufficiency and not _____. God's sufficiency is more than enough.

    b.   The grace life depends on you letting Christ's life live in and through you. It's not yours life, but His life that carries you.

    c.   Grace is not what _____ do, but what Christ has done. Let Christ's life, His power, His love, His behavior, His passion, His sufficiency flow through you that others might see the heart of the Father.

    d.   It's believing, surrendering, and _____ Christ's life, power, love, behavior, passion and sufficiency and letting it flow in and through you.

C.   The Old Covenant is _____.

Hebrews 8:13 (ESV)
¹³In speaking of a new covenant, He makes the first one obsolete. And what is becoming obsolete and growing old is ready to vanish away.

Answers: yours, you, receiving, obsolete

James 2:10 (NIV)

[10]*For whoever keeps the whole law and yet stumbles at just one point is guilty of breaking all of it.*

Romans 12:2 (NIV)

[2]*Do not conform to the pattern of this world, but be transformed by the renewing of your mind. Then you will be able to test and approve what God's will is—His good, pleasing and perfect will.*

Hebrew 11:33 (TPT)

[33]*Through faith's power they conquered kingdoms and established true justice. Their faith fastened onto their promises and pulled them into reality! It was faith that shut the mouth of lions.*

Ephesians 1:11b (TPT)

[11]*Before we were even born, He gave us our destiny; that we would fulfill the plan of God Who always accomplishes every purpose and plan in His heart.* **<in the invisible>**

2 Peter 1:4 (NIV)

[4]*Through these He has given us His very great and precious promises, so that through them you may participate in the divine nature, having escaped the corruption in the world caused by evil desires.*

Hebrews 4:11 (NIV)

[11]*Let us, therefore, make every effort to enter that rest, so that no one will perish by following their example of disobedience.*

John 17:6, 8 (NIV)

[6]*I have revealed You to those whom you gave Me out of the world. They were yours; You gave them to Me and they have obeyed Your Word.* [8]*For I gave them the words You gave Me and they accepted them. They knew with certainty that I came from You, and they believed that You sent Me.*

John 14:9 (NIV)
[9] *Jesus answered: "Don't you know Me, Philip, even after I have been among you such a long time? Anyone who has seen Me has seen the Father. How can you say, 'Show us the Father'?"*

John 6:29 (NIV)
[29] *Jesus answered, "The work of God is this: to believe in the One He has sent."*

Point #3 Do we see Father God as the Moral Police of the Universe?

A. **A Father God Who is _____ for failures we might commit, at any moment, to punish us.**

    1.   A Father God Who puts sickness, poverty and storms in your life to make you better?

    2.   A Father God Who kills you because He _____ you in heaven?

John 10:10 (NKJ)
[10] *The thief does not come except to steal, and to kill, and to destroy. I have come that they may have life, and that they may have it more abundantly.*

1 John 4:18 (NIV)
[18] *There is no fear in love. But perfect love drives out fear, because fear has to do with punishment. The one who fears is not made perfect in love.*

Answers: watching, needs

Romans 4:15-16 (NIV)
15because the law brings wrath. And where there is no law there is no transgression. 16Therefore, the promise comes by faith, so that it may be by grace and may be guaranteed to all Abraham's offspring—not only to those who are of the law but also to those who have the faith of Abraham. He is the father of us all.

Luke 8:17 (NIV)
17For there is nothing hidden that will not be disclosed, and nothing concealed that will not be known or brought out into the open.

B. Jesus says, "_____ them for they know not what they do".

1. Jesus forgave our _____, present and future sins.

Luke 23:34 (NIV)
34 Jesus said, "Father, forgive them, for they do not know what they are doing."

2. This kind of forgiveness is a _____ of grace.

C. Every blessing from our Father God finds its source in His grace. (Rom. 8:28)

1. It's grace that changes our _____ and not the law that changes us.

Answers: Forgive, past, picture, hearts

45

Ezekiel 36: 26-27 (NIV)

26I will give you a new heart and put a new spirit in you; I will remove from you your heart of stone and give you a heart of flesh. 27And I will put my Spirit in you and move you to follow My decrees and be careful to keep My laws.

D. Our Father God _____ hold our sins against us or remember them anymore. This is grace!

Romans 4:7-8 (AMP)

7Blessed and happy and favored are those whose lawless acts have been forgiven, and whose sins have been covered up and completely buried. 8Blessed and happy and favored is the man whose sin the Lord will not take into account nor charge against him.

1. Jesus _____ a loving Father Who loved us while we were yet sinners.

2. Our Father God's blessings aren't a result of our faithfulness, but because of Father God's faithfulness.

3. Father God doesn't bless us because of how wonderful we are, but because of how wonderful Father _____ is!

Romans 8:17 (TPT)

17And since we are His true children, we qualify to share all His treasures, for indeed we are heirs of God Himself, and since we are joined to Christ, we also inherit all that He is and all that He has.

E. Let's talk about King _____.

Answers: doesn't, reveals, God, David

Acts 2:25-31 (NKJ)

^{25}*For David says concerning Him:*

"I foresaw the Lord always before my face, for He is at my right hand, that I may not be shaken. ^{26} Therefore my heart rejoiced, and my tongue was glad; moreover my flesh also will rest in hope. ^{27}For You will not leave my soul in Hades, nor will You allow Your Holy One to see corruption. ^{28}You have made known to me the ways of life; You will make me full of joy in Your presence."

^{29}*"Men and brethren, let me speak freely to you of the patriarch David, that he is both dead and buried, and his tomb is with us to this day."*

^{30}*Therefore, being a prophet, and knowing that God had sworn with an oath to him that of the fruit of his body, according to the flesh, He would raise up the Christ to sit on His throne, ^{31}he, foreseeing this, spoke concerning the resurrection of the Christ, that His soul was not left in Hades, nor did His flesh see corruption.*

1. King David _____ the death, burial, and resurrection of Christ Jesus in his lifetime.

2. King David saw the New Covenant of God.

3. God is the Alpha and _____. He finished then He began in the invisible.

4. King David _____ and received the Covenant of Grace.

5. King David had an affair with Bathsheba, and she became pregnant. He had her husband killed and then he married her.

6. King David _____ and then Bathsheba had Solomon.

Answers: saw, Omega, believed, repented

47

See 2 Samuel, Chapters 11-12

a. King Solomon was the wisest and richest king on the _____!

1 Kings 10:23 (NKJV)
23So King Solomon surpassed all the kings of the earth in riches and wisdom.

b. There was an older brother in line to be king, but in _____, God chose Solomon, a picture of grace.

See 1 Kings 1:5-40

Romans 8:28 (NKJ)
28And we know that all things work together for good to those who love God, to those who are called according to His purpose.

F. God is <u>not</u> the moral _____ of the universe.

Hebrew 2:17-18 (NKJ)
17Therefore, in all things He had to be made like His brethren, that He might be a merciful and faithful High Priest in things pertaining to God, to make propitiation for the sins of the people. 18For in that He Himself has suffered, being tempted, He is able to aid those who are tempted.

Hebrews 4:15 (NKJ)
15For we do not have a High Priest Who cannot sympathize with our weaknesses, but was in all points tempted as we are, yet without sin.

Answers: earth, grace, policeman

John 13:34 (NKJ)

34A new commandment I give to you, that you love one another; as I have loved you, that you also love one another.

Romans 8:17 (NKJ)

17and if children, then heirs—heirs of God and joint heirs with Christ, if indeed we suffer with Him, that we may also be glorified together.

G.   Father God says, "I _____"… That is the meaning of grace.

1.   It's not about what we've done, but about what our loving Father has _____ as a result of His love for us.

2.   The grace walk doesn't depend on our feeble efforts, but on Father God's _____ empowerment within us.

3.   Legalism redirects the focus from Father God to _____. It's seeing God as a stern judge and not as a loving Father.

Hebrews 8:7-12 (NIV)

7For if there had been nothing wrong with that first covenant, no place would have been sought for another. 8But God found fault with the people and said:
"The days are coming," declares the Lord, "When I will make a new covenant with the people of Israel and with the people of Judah. 9It will not be like the covenant I made with their ancestors when I took them by the hand to lead them out of Egypt, because they did not remain faithful to my covenant, and I turned away from them, declares the Lord. 10This covenant I will establish with the people of Israel after that time, declares the Lord. I will put my laws in their minds and write them

Answers: will, done, faithful, self

49

on their hearts. I will be their God and they will be My people. [11]No longer will they teach their neighbor, or say to one another, 'Know the Lord,' because they will all know Me, from the least of them to the greatest. [12]For I will forgive their wickedness and will remember their sins no more."

H. The meaning of Grace is Father God _____ do... Which is exactly what He did!

    1.   -   <u>I will</u> effect a new covenant.

         -   <u>I will</u> put my laws into their_____.

         -   <u>I will</u> _____ them upon their hearts.

         -   <u>I will</u> be their God.

         -   <u>I will</u> be _____to their iniquities.

         -   <u>I will</u> remember their sins _____more.

    2.   God said, "I will..." in the Abrahamic Covenant

         -   <u>I will</u> make you a great_____.

         -   <u>I will</u> make your name great.

         -   <u>I will</u> _____you.

         -   I will defeat of your enemies.

         -   <u>I will</u> _____those who bless you.

Answers: will, minds, write, merciful, no, nation, bless, bless

In Christ, We Always Win
Chapter 6

Point #1 Do we see Father God as the Stern Boss, not our Loving Father?

A. Do we see Father God as_____, demanding, distant, and brutal at times?

B. Do we see Him as a stern boss who says, "It's never good enough?"

Ephesians 1:3 (TPT)

3Every spiritual blessing in the heavenly realm has already been lavished upon us as a love gift from our wonderful heavenly Father, the Father of our Lord Jesus—all because He sees us wrapped into Christ. This is why we celebrate Him with all our hearts!

1 John 3:1 (NIV)

1See what great love the Father has lavished on us, that we should be called children of God! And that is what we are! The reason the world does not know us is that it did not know Him.

C. Do we see God through a _____ perspective Who gives no room for enjoying life?

Point #2 Prodigal Son

A. The Prodigal Son is a perfect _____ of legalism and grace.

Answers: harsh,   legalistic,   picture

Luke 15:11-28 (NKJ)

[11]Then He said:

"A certain man had two sons. [12]And the younger of them said to his father,

'Father, give me the portion of goods that falls to me.'

So he divided to them his livelihood. [13]And not many days after, the younger son gathered all together, journeyed to a far country, and there wasted his possessions with prodigal living. [14]But when he had spent all, there arose a severe famine in that land, and he began to be in want. [15]Then he went and joined himself to a citizen of that country, and he sent him into his fields to feed swine. [16]And he would gladly have filled his stomach with the pods that the swine ate, and no one gave him anything.

[17]"But when he came to himself, he said,

'How many of my father's hired servants have bread enough and to spare, and I perish with hunger! [18]I will arise and go to my father, and will say to him,

"Father, I have sinned against heaven and before you, [19]and I am no longer worthy to be called your son. Make me like one of your hired servants."'

[20]"And he arose and came to his father. But when he was still a great way off, his father saw him and had compassion, and ran and fell on his neck and kissed him. [21]And the son said to him,

'Father, I have sinned against heaven and in your sight, and am no longer worthy to be called your son.'

[22]"But the father said to his servants,

'Bring out the best robe and put it on him, and put a ring on his hand and sandals on his feet. [23]And bring the fatted calf here and kill it, and let us eat and be merry; [24] for this my son was dead and is alive again; he was lost and is found.'

And they began to be merry.

25 "Now his older son was in the field. And as he came and drew near to the house, he heard music and dancing. 26So he called one of the servants and asked what these things meant. 27And he said to him, 'Your brother has come, and because he has received him safe and sound, your father has killed the fatted calf.'
28 "But he was angry and would not go in. Therefore his father came out and pleaded with him."

1.   The oldest son is a picture of _____ believers and legalism.

2.   The younger son is a picture of _____.

B.   Grace is not a license to sin, but grace gives us the _____ and ability NOT to sin.

Titus 2:11-12 (NIV)
11For the grace of God has appeared that offers salvation to all people. 12It teaches us to say "No" to ungodliness and worldly passions, and to live self-controlled, upright and godly lives in this present age.

C.   The younger son was filled with condemnation, guilt, and _____.

Galatians 6:8 (NKJ)
8For he who sows to his flesh will of the flesh reap corruption, but he who sows to the Spirit will of the Spirit reap everlasting life.

Luke 15:20 (NIV)
20So he got up and went to his father. But while he was still a long way off, his father saw him and was filled with compassion for him; he ran to his son, threw his arms around him and kissed him. **<No judgment, no condemnation, shame or guilt from the father.>**

Answers: religious, grace, power, shame

1. We think God punishes sin. No! _____ punishes sin.

2. The father of the Prodigal Son is a picture of Father God, Abba, Daddy toward us.

    a. The father had a_____ on his mind, a celebration full of laughter, fun, and joy.

John 10:10 (NKJ)
I have come that they may have life, and that they may have it more abundantly.

    b. Father God has _____ in abundance for us, more than we expect and a fullness that overflows!

John 10:10 (TPT)
But I have come to give you everything in abundance, more than you expect – life in its fullness until you overflow.

Matthew 11:19 (NKJ)
¹⁹The Son of Man came eating and drinking, and they say, "Look, a glutton and a wine-bibber, a friend of tax collectors and sinners!" But wisdom is justified by her children.

3. To the _____ crowd everything was sin, and Jesus never sinned.

Galatians 6:8b (TPT)
⁸If you plant the corrupt seeds of self-life into this natural realm, you can expect to experience a harvest of corruption.

Answers: Sin, party, everything, religious

54

Luke 15:21 (NIV)

21The son said to him, "Father, I have sinned against heaven and against you. I am no longer worthy to be called your son."

    4.   The father _____ his son with excitement and joy. He threw a party for his son and brought him into son ship with him.

Luke 15:22-24 (NIV)

22But the father said to his servants, "Quick! Bring the best robe and put it on him. Put a ring on his finger and sandals on his feet. 23Bring the fattened calf and kill it. Let's have a feast and celebrate. 24For this son of mine was dead and is alive again; he was lost and is found." So they began to celebrate.

    5.   The ring symbolizes _____.

Matthew 28:18 (NKJ)

18And Jesus came and spoke to them, saying, "All authority has been given to Me in heaven and on earth."

D.   God's Kingdom is _____! It's celebrating and party time! Jesus was fun and a partier.

Ephesians 5:18 (NIV)

18Do not get drunk on wine, which leads to debauchery. Instead, be filled with the Spirit.

    1.   The early _____ had house-to-house fellowship, and fellowship is *Koinonia* in Greek meaning party and fellowship.

Answers: received, authority, fun, church

Isaiah 65:14 (NIV)

14 My servants will sing out of the joy of their hearts

2.   This means:

   a.   Singing

   b.   _____on God's Word, which is the best food ever!

   c.   It's a family time of love, fun and laughter.

3.   The Day of Pentecost was a _____, a celebration in God with no wine.

Acts 2:12-13 (NIV)

12Amazed and perplexed, they asked one another, "What does this mean?" 13Some, however, made fun of them and said, "They have had too much wine."

4.   We've been given life and life more _____.

Life, love, joy!
You are in Christ, so join the party!
Loosen up and live!
_____the celebration.
Go ahead and let go.
Believe, live and sing in the Covenant of Grace.

Ecclesiastes 9:7 (NIV)

7Go, eat your food with gladness, and drink your wine with a joyful heart, for God has already approved what you do.

Answers: Feasting, party, abundant, Enjoy

E. God is the Restorer of what the canker worm has eaten in your life.

   1.   It's time to _____.

   2.   It's time to believe for seven times what the devil has stolen. This is the mercy of God.

Proverbs 8:30-31 (NKJ)
[30]Then I was beside Him as a master craftsman; and I was daily His delight, rejoicing always before Him, [3]Rejoicing in His inhabited world, and My delight was with the sons of men.

F.   In the life of _____, we find:

   1.   Protection

   2.   _____

   3.   Time of fellowship

   4.   _____

   5.   Knitting together in love

Ephesians 2:19-20 (NKJ)
[19]Now, therefore, you are no longer strangers and foreigners, but fellow citizens with the saints and members of the household of God, [20]having been built on the foundation of the apostles and prophets, Jesus Christ Himself being the chief cornerstone.

G.   The Holy Spirit will let you know if you are going the _____ way.

Answers: rebuild, grace, Security, Family, wrong

Isaiah 30:21 (NKJ)

²¹*Your ears shall hear a word behind you, saying, "This is the way, walk in it," Whenever you turn to the right hand or whenever you turn to the left.*

1. God's _____ keeps no record of wrongs.

1 Corinthians 13:5 (NIV)

⁵**(love)** *keeps no record of wrongs.*

H. Pictures are given of the older and younger brothers.

1. The older brother is a picture of a person living under the Old Covenant or under the _____.

2. The younger brother is a picture of a person living under the New Covenant or _____.

Luke 15:29-30 (NIV)

²⁹*But he answered his father, "Look! All these years I've been slaving for you and never disobeyed your orders. Yet you never gave me even a young goat so I could celebrate with my friends. ³⁰But when this son of yours who has squandered your property with prostitutes comes home, you kill the fattened calf for him!"*

3. The older brother has an obsessive-compulsive _____ to the law.

   a. There is _____ party or fun in legalism.

   b. There's only judgment, condemnation, shame, guilt and death in legalism.

Answers: love, law, grace, connection, no,

<But Jesus ran _____ sinners with love and freedom.>

     c.   Legalists are all about the_____, not the relationship.

     d.   Grace does not condone sinful behavior nor does it punish sin.

        1.   _____ punishes sin.

Galatians 6:8 (TPT)
⁸If you plant the corrupt seeds of self-life into this natural realm, you can expect to experience a harvest of corruption.

Point #3 God is a loving Father Who delights in you.

Psalm 16:3 (NKJ)
³As for the saints who are on the earth, "They are the excellent ones, **(we fulfill all of God's desires)** *in Whom is all My delight."*

Zephaniah 3:17 (AMP)
¹⁷The Lord your God is in your midst, a Warrior Who saves. He will rejoice over you with joy; He will be quiet in His love [making no mention of your past sins], He will rejoice over you with shouts of joy.

A.   God is a loving Father Who is _____ with you, a loving Father Who is overwhelmed with joy because you are His, a loving Father Who is unable to contain His emotions for you; He shouts for joy when He looks at you!

Answers: toward, rules, Sin, thrilled

I John 3:1a (NIV)

3See what great love the Father has lavished on us, that we should be called children of God!

Proverbs 8:30-31 (NKJ)

30Then I was beside Him as a master craftsman; and I was daily His delight, (pleasure) rejoicing always before Him, 31Rejoicing in His inhabited world, and My delight (pleasure) was with the sons of men.

Romans 8:35-39 (NIV)

35Who shall separate us from the love of Christ? Shall trouble or hardship or persecution or famine or nakedness or danger or sword? 36As it is written:

"For your sake we face death all day long; we are considered as sheep to be slaughtered."

37No, in all these things we are more than conquerors through Him Who loved us. 38For I am convinced that neither death nor life, neither angels nor demons neither the present nor the future, nor any powers, 39neither height nor depth, nor anything else in all creation, will be able to separate us from the love of God that is in Christ Jesus our Lord.

Romans 5:15 (NKJ)

15But the free gift is not like the offense. For if by the one man's offense many died, much more the grace of God and the gift by the grace of the one Man, Jesus Christ, abounded to many.

Romans 8:39 (TPT)

29There is no power above us or beneath us – no power that could ever be found in the universe that can distance us from God's passionate love, which is lavished upon us through our Lord Jesus, the Anointed One!

1.   God is a loving Father Who has not _____ one
      thing in the Kingdom from us.

**Imagine a loving Father looking at _____.
His eyes are filled with joy, delight, He's smiling, laughing out
loud. _____ are the reason for His happiness.
He adores you, enjoys you, celebrates you, favors you,
And loves you with His complete love.
And this _____ changes.**

THIS IS GRACE

2 Corinthians 4:18 (NKJ)
18while we do not look at the things which are seen, but at the things which are not seen. For the things which are seen are temporary, but the things which are not seen are eternal.

Point #4 The New Covenant is a Covenant of Grace.

**A.   The Apostle Paul received the revelation of _____
from Jesus Christ. (Not from man).**

Galatians 1:11-12 (NIV)
11I want you to know, brothers and sisters, that the gospel I preached is not of human origin. 12I did not receive it from any man, nor was I taught it; rather, I received it by revelation from Jesus Christ.

1.   Let's look at an examination of the differences between the
      Old and New_____.

Answers: withheld, you, You, never, revelation, Covenants

John 1:17 (NKJ)

17For the law was given through Moses, but grace and truth came through Jesus Christ.

Galatians 3:10 (NKJ)

10For as many as are of the works of the law are under the curse; for it is written, "Cursed is everyone who does not continue in all things which are written in the book of the law, to do them."

B.   The Old Covenant was

1.   _____.

2.   Bilateral, two-sided, between God and _____.

3.   Temporal.

C.   The New Covenant is

1.   _____.

2.   Unilateral, one-sided, between God and God (_____).

3.   Eternal.

Galatians 3:17 (TPT)

17...the covenant between God and Abraham was fulfilled in Messiah and cannot be altered.

Galatians 3:8 (NKJ)

8And the Scripture foreseeing that God would justify the Gentiles by faith preached the Gospel to Abraham beforehand...

Answers: Conditional, man, Unconditional, Jesus

1 Timothy 2:4 (NKJ)
⁴Who desires all men to be saved and to come to the knowledge of the truth.

Revelation 13:8 (NKJ)
⁸...the Lamb slain from the foundation of the world.

Romans 4:3 (NKJ)
³For what does the Scripture say? "Abraham believed God, and it was accounted to him for righteousness."

Galatians 3:20 (TPT)
²⁰Now, a mediator does not represent just one party alone, but God fulfilled it all by Himself!

Galatians 3:9 (TPT)
⁹And so the blessing of Abraham's faith is now our blessing too.

Matthew 9:17 (NIV)
¹⁷Neither do people pour new wine into old wineskins. If they do, the skins will burst; the wine will run out and the wineskins will be ruined. No, they pour new wine into new wineskins, and both are preserved.

Ephesians 3:9 (TPT)
⁹My passion is to enlighten every person to this divine mystery. It was hidden for ages past until now, and kept a secret in the heart of God, the Creator of all.

1 Corinthians 15:10 (NIV)
¹⁰But by the grace of God I am what I am, and His grace to me was not without effect. No, I worked harder than all of them—yet not I, but the grace of God that was with me.

Romans 7:4 (NKJ)

[4]*Therefore, my brethren, you also have become dead to the law through the body of Christ, that you may be married to another—to Him Who was raised from the dead, that we should bear fruit to God.*

Jeremiah 31:33-34 (NIV)

[33]*"This is the covenant I will make with the people of Israel after that time," declares the LORD. "I will put My law in their minds and write it on their hearts. I will be their God, and they will be My people.* [34]*No longer will they teach their neighbor, or say to one another, 'Know the LORD,' because they will all know Me, from the least of them to the greatest," declares the LORD. "For I will forgive their wickedness and will remember their sins no more."*

D.   The New Covenant is unconditional because it lacks the word, "_____." We are not in the equation. It's all about God's will. Our part is to believe and receive.

      1.   The <u>Old Covenant</u> was blessing and _____.

          a.   The responsibility was on _____.

      2.   The <u>New Covenant</u> is blessing and _____.

E.   The New Covenant is one-sided because all responsibility is on _____, and we are all in Christ.

F.   It's eternal – unending because it's not based on our works but on _____ works.

Answers: if, cursing, us, blessing, God, Christ's

The New Covenant couldn't be effective or operate until the curse of the Old Covenant was paid in full. The New Covenant is without the possibility of human failure ending it so the promises will never _____ because the covenant is eternal and unending.

Answers: fail

From Blessing to Blessing
Chapter 7

Point #1 Paul is so angry at the false teachers.

A. **The New Covenant takes us from blessing to _____.**

Romans 11:5-6 (NKJ)
⁵*Even so then, at this present time there is a remnant according to the election of grace.* ⁶*And if by grace, then it is no longer of works; otherwise grace is no longer grace. But if it is of works, it is no longer grace; otherwise work is no longer work.*

Genesis 1:22 (NIV)
²²*God blessed them and said, "Be _____ and increase in number and fill the water in the seas, and let the birds increase on the earth..."*

B. **There is only _____ Gospel.**

Luke 24:51 (NIV)
⁵¹*While He was blessing them, He left them and was taken up into heaven.*

Luke 24:51 (TPT)
⁵¹*While He was still speaking out words of love and blessing, He floated off the ground into the sky, ascending into heaven before their very eyes!*

1. The New Covenant could not be effective until the _____ of the Old Covenant was paid in full.

Answers: blessing, fruitful, one, curse

66

2. Under the Covenant of Grace, <New Covenant> the works of Christ, we _____, submit and receive and let it flow.

Ephesians 1:11 (TPT)

¹¹This is why God selected and ordained us to be His own inheritance through our union with Christ! Before we were even born, He gave us our destiny; that we would fulfill the plan of God Who always accomplishes every purpose and plan in His heart.

Ephesians 3:20 (TPT)

²⁰Never doubt God's mighty power to work in you and accomplish all this. He will achieve infinitely more than your greatest request, your most unbelievable dream and exceed your wildest imagination!

   a. We need a paradigm shift from the Old to the New Covenant.

      1. The Old Covenant was based on what _____ did.

      2. The New Covenant is based on what _____ did.

   b. We don't fight for the blessings.

   c. The _____ fight for us.

   d. You are in Christ, a co-heir, now.

<Christ is full of grace and blessings, and in Christ, we are full of grace and blessings.>

Answers: believe, we, Christ, blessings

Galatians 3:14 (TPT)

14...all the blessings of Abraham can be poured out upon even non-Jewish believers.

Galatians 1:6-7 (NKJV)

6I marvel that you are turning away so soon from Him Who called you in the grace of Christ, to a different gospel, 7which is not another; but there are some who trouble you and want to pervert the Gospel of Christ.

3. Paul was saying the Old Covenant is non-_____.

Galatians 1:7 (TPT)

7That is a fake "gospel" that is simply not true. There is only one Gospel-the Gospel of the Messiah! Yet you have allowed those who mingle the law with grace to confuse you with lies.

4. We can become confused with _____.

5. There is only one Gospel, the Gospel of the Messiah, what Christ has already _____.

Deuteronomy 28:1-2 (NKJ)

1Now it shall come to pass, if you diligently obey the voice of the LORD your God, to observe carefully all His commandments which I command you today, that the LORD your God will set you high above all nations of the earth. 2And all these blessings shall come upon you and overtake you, because you obey the voice of the LORD your God...

6. _____ cannot carefully observe all His commandments, but Christ did! We are in His works as co-heirs.

Answers: existent, lies, done, You

68

Deuteronomy 28:7 (NKJ)

⁷The LORD will cause your enemies who rise against you to be defeated before your face; they shall come out against you one way and flee before you seven ways.

    a.   The enemy is a _____ who brings the curse of the law.

<The blessings _____ for you.>

    b.   Through Jesus, you _____ the blessings, forgiveness, and the armor of God.

Galatians 1:8 (NKJ)

⁸But even if we, or an angel from heaven, preach any other gospel to you than what we have preached to you, let him be accursed.

    7.   Accursed means to be _____ to destruction.

Galatians 3:10 (TPT)

¹⁰But if you choose to live in bondage under the legalistic rule of religion, you live under the law's curse.

Deuteronomy 6:10-12 (NKJ)

¹⁰So it shall be, when the LORD your God brings you into the land of which He swore to your fathers, to Abraham, Isaac, and Jacob, to give you large and beautiful cities which you did not build, ¹¹houses full of all good things, which you did not fill, hewn-out wells which you did not dig, vineyards and olive trees which you did not plant—when you have eaten and are full— ¹²then beware, lest you forget the LORD Who brought you out of the land of Egypt, from the house of bondage.

Answers: bully, fight, inherit, devoted

Galatians 6:8 (TPT)

⁸If you plant the corrupt seeds of self-life (**sin conscious → self-conscious→ focus on self and not Jesus**) *into this natural realm, you can expect to experience a harvest of corruption. If you plant the good seeds of the Spirit-life, you will reap the beautiful fruits that grow from the everlasting life of the Spirit.*

2 Peter 1:4 (NIV)

⁴Through these He has given us His very great and precious promises, so that through them you may participate in the divine nature, having escaped the corruption in the world caused by evil desires.

\<The blessings fight for you!\>

Ecclesiastes 5:19 (NIV)

¹⁹Moreover, when God gives someone wealth and possessions, and the ability to enjoy them, to accept their lot and be happy in their toil—this is a gift of God.

Galatians 3:18 (TPT)

¹⁸The law, then, doesn't supersede the promise since the royal proclamation was given before the law. If that were the case, it would have nullified what God said to Abraham. We receive all the promises because of the Promised One—not because we keep the law!

Galatians 3:10 (TPT)

¹⁰But if you choose to live in bondage under the legalistic rule of religion, you live under the law's curse. For it is clearly written: "Utterly cursed is everyone who fails to practice every detail and requirement that is written in this law!"

    8.   Under the _____, we are cursed.

Answers: law

Point #2 Paul Received Heart Revelation

Galatians 1:11-12 (NIV)

¹¹I want you to know, brothers and sisters, that the gospel I preached is not of human origin. ¹²I did not receive it from any man, nor was I taught it; rather, I received it by <u>revelation</u> from Jesus Christ.

The word <u>revelation</u> in Greek means the "unveiling of the otherwise unknown, to lighten, by the _____ of the Holy Spirit."

A.   The people had head knowledge, but not _____ revelation of the New Covenant.

    1.   The picture in their hearts was religious and legalistic.

    2.   What's in our hearts is what we will _____.

        a.   Ask the question: "What am I producing?"

        b.   You need revelation of _____.

    3.   The Old Covenant is of the natural but the New Covenant is _____.

Galatians 4:23-24 (TPT)

²³Ishmael, the son of the slave girl, was a child of the natural realm. But Isaac, the son of the free woman, was born supernaturally by the Spirit – a child of the promise of God! ²⁴These two women and their sons expressed an allegory and become symbols of two covenants.

Answers: supernatural, heart, produce, grace, supernatural

B. **Because the New Covenant is supernatural, it has to come by**
_____

    1.   Paul _____ for revelation for the people.

Ephesians 1:17 (NIV)
¹⁷I keep asking that the God of our Lord Jesus Christ, the glorious Father, may give you the Spirit of wisdom and revelation, so that you may know Him better.

John 1:16 (NIV84)
From the fullness of His grace we have all received one blessing after another.

Galatians 3:8 (TPT)
⁸God's plan all along was to bring this message of salvation to the nations through the revelation of faith…

    2.   We have the _____ of Christ Jesus.

Hebrews 12:2 (NKJ)
²looking unto Jesus, the Author and Finisher of our faith…

<Humble Yourself - Be Real>

    3.   The Faith of Christ takes us to a realm that _____ cannot take ourselves.

Genesis 15:1 (NIV)
¹After this, the word of the Lord came to Abram in a vision, "Do not be afraid, Abram, I AM your shield, your very great reward."

Answers: revelation, prayed, faith, we

Ephesians 6:16 (NKJ)
¹⁶ above all, taking the shield of faith with which you will be able to quench all the fiery darts of the wicked one.

Galatians 3:5 (TPT)
⁵ ...the Holy Spirit is poured out upon us through the revelation and power of faith, not by keeping the law!

4.   The Holy Spirit is poured out upon <u>you</u> through the
_____ and power of faith, not by keeping
the law.

Romans 5:2 (NIV)
²Through Whom we have gained access by faith into this grace in which we now stand.

Mark 9:23-24 (NIV)
²³"If you can?" said Jesus. "Everything is possible for one who believes." ²⁴Immediately the boy's father exclaimed, "I do believe; help me overcome my unbelief!"

a.   God gives _____ to the humble.

James 4:6 (NKJ)
⁶But He gives more grace. Therefore, He says: "God resists the proud, but gives grace to the humble."

Answers: revelation, grace

The Blessings are Working for You
Chapter 8

Point #1 The Old Covenant is of the Natural, but the New Covenant is Supernatural

Galatians 4:23-24 (TPT)
²³Ishamel, the son of the slave girl, was a child of the natural realm. But Isaac, the son of the free woman, was born supernaturally by the Spirit – a child of the promise of God! ²⁴These two women and their sons express an allegory and become symbols of two covenants.

A.   The Old Covenant makes us _____ conscious.

   1.   We look at what we see in the natural.

   2.   Ishmael was a child of the natural realm. In the Old Covenant, we cannot see by the _____.

   3.   Isaac was a child by the free woman (picture of New Covenant). In the New Covenant, we can see into the _____, supernatural realm.

Mark 9:23-24 (NIV)
²³"If you can?" said Jesus. "Everything is possible for one who believes." ²⁴Immediately the boy's father exclaimed, "I do believe; help me overcome my unbelief!"

B.   The New Covenant makes us _____ conscious.

   1.   We look at what He has already done in the unseen.

Answers: sin, Spirit, unseen, Christ

    a.   God gives _____ to the humble.

    b.   The faith of _____ takes us into a
         realm that we cannot take ourselves.

C.   We need to keep our eyes on Jesus.

    1.   I see blessing and blessing because _____
         was full of grace.

    2.   What we see, we become.

Point #2 Understanding the New Covenant of Grace, A Covenant of the Supernatural

Galatians 3:1 (NIV84)
¹You foolish Galatians, who has bewitched you, before whose eyes Jesus Christ was publicly portrayed as crucified?

Galatians 3:1 (TPT)
¹You must have been under some evil spell! Didn't God open your eyes to see the meaning of Jesus' crucifixion?

A.   The great revelation of the cross had been spoken to them; but they were _____ the glorious work of the cross by adding the works of religion. They were holding onto religious beliefs.

    1.   In living under the Old Covenant,

        a.   They apparently hadn't made the great _____.

Answers: grace, Christ, Jesus, diluting, exchange

75

2. In the New Covenant, I bind myself to the promises of God.

   a. I bind myself to what Christ has done.

   b. _____ myself to the promises of God.

   c. The supernatural is powerfully _____ in my life.

Point #3 Men and women of the faith of Christ are the ones who live in the blessings.

Romans 5:2 (NIV)
²...through Whom we have gained access by faith into this grace in which we now stand.

A. Grace is accessed by _____. Faith worketh by love.

Galatians 5:6 (NKJ)
⁶For in Christ Jesus neither circumcision nor uncircumcision avails anything, but faith working through love.

   1. Faith works through love.

      a. _____ of love.

      b. Words of love.

      c. Actions of love.

   2. God is_____!

Answers: Fastening, working, faith, Thoughts, love

1 John 4:8 (NIV)

⁸ Whoever does not love does not know God, because God is love.

    a.   The love of God puts faith into _____ to bring what is in the unseen to the seen.

Hebrews 4:12 (NIV)

*¹²For the Word of God **(Christ Jesus)** is alive and active. Sharper than any double-edged sword, it penetrates even to dividing <u>soul and spirit</u>, joints and marrow; it judges the thoughts and attitudes of the heart.*

The Word will *penetrate even to dividing <u>soul and spirit</u>* which means to be _____ led and not emotionally driven.

Galatians 3:9 (TPT)

⁹And so the blessing of Abraham's faith is now our blessing too!

    3.   From the _____ of His grace, Christ Jesus, we go from blessing to blessing.

B.   Take on the _____ of Christ, "His mind."

    1.   Christ's thoughts are thoughts of blessings.

    2.   Christ's thoughts are _____ for us to the abundance.

    3.   Christ's thoughts are going from love to love.

    4.   Christ's thoughts go from _____ to favor.

    5.   Christ's thoughts are conquering to conquering.

Answers: action, Spirit, fullness, thoughts, life, favor

6. Christ's thoughts go from wealth to _____.

7. Christ's thoughts are seeing signs and wonders in _____ area of our lives and in others.

Matthew 10:8 (NKJ)
⁸Heal the sick, cleanse the lepers, raise the dead, cast out demons. Freely you have received, freely give.

Genesis 12:2 (NKJ)
²I will make you a great nation; I will bless you and make your name great; and you shall be a blessing.

C. Christ tames your _____ with the sword of the Spirit.

1. Your _____ is full of miracles.

Hebrews 11:3 (NKJ)
³By faith we understand that the worlds were framed by the Word of God, so that the things which are seen were not made of things which are visible.

D. If you _____ to live in legalistic bondage, that's what you will produce.

Galatians 3:10 (TPT)
But if you choose to live in bondage under the legalistic rule of religion, you live under the law's curse. For it is clearly written: "Utterly cursed is everyone who fails to practice every detail and requirement that is written in this law!"

Answers: wealth, every, tongue, mouth, choose

E. Job was in fear.

    1.   He was totally _____ to the law.

        a.   The law speaks of punishment and fear.

        b.   There is no _____ in fear.

    2.   The law is fear driven.

The law is what _____ do, not what Christ has done.

Galatians 3:12 (TPT)

[12]*But keeping the law does not require faith, but* **<u>self-effort</u>***. For the law teaches, "If you practice the principles of the law, you must follow all of them."*

Galatians 3:13 (TPT)

[13]*Yet, Christ paid the full price* **(It is finished.)** *to set us free from the curse of the law. He absorbed it completely as He became a curse in our place. For it is written: "Everyone who is hung upon a tree is doubly cursed."*

Galatians 3:14 (TPT)

[14]*Jesus, our Messiah, was cursed in our place and in so doing, dissolved the curse from our lives, so that all the blessings of Abraham can be poured out upon even non-Jewish believers. And now God gives us the promise of the wonderful Holy Spirit Who lives within us when we believe in Him.*

Deuteronomy 30:19 (NIV)

[19]*This day I call the heavens and the earth as witnesses against you that I have set before you life and death, blessings and curses. Now choose life, so that you and your children may live*

Answers: committed, love, you

79

3.   You have _____ to choose.

F.   God is looking for people to _____ what Christ has already done.

G.   This is how the system operates. Faith is what Christ has done. You fasten yourself to the _____.

1.   This is how grace is, _____ choose.

   a.   Choose faith or law.

   b.   Choose life or _____.

   c.   Choose blessing or curses.

Hosea 6:6 (NIV)
⁶For I desire mercy, not sacrifice, and acknowledgment of God rather than burnt offerings.

H.   The law _____ obedience in all things.

1.   You must do all without any compromise.

2.   You are _____ a law-keeper or a law-breaker.

3.   It is an absolute standard.

4.   Even one little _____ can mar your record.

Answers: freedom, embrace, promises, you, death, demands, either, error

a. Just as one spot of jam spoils the wedding dress, and one nail flattens the tire, so one broken commandment spoils you, and then comes the flood of the _____. This is not good.

Point #4 What are the alternatives? There are only two here: your righteousness or Christ's righteousness.

A. We can't be _____ enough to be righteous or earn our own righteousness.

Galatians 2:21 (NIV)
21 I do not set aside **(frustrate, nullify)** *the grace* **(what Christ has done)** *of God, for if righteousness could be gained through the law* **(what we do)**, *Christ died for nothing!"* **(no purpose, in vain)**

Romans 9:30-32 (NIV)
30What then shall we say? That the Gentiles, who did not pursue righteousness, have obtained it, a righteousness that is by faith; 31but the people of Israel, who pursued the law as the way of righteousness, have not attained their goal. 32Why not? Because they pursued it not by faith but as if it were by works.

1. When we are in our own righteousness, we can't _____ to God's righteousness.

Romans 10:3 (NIV)
3Since they did not know the righteousness of God and sought to establish their own, they did not submit to God's righteousness.

Answers: curse, good, submit

81

Romans 10:3 (TPT)

³And since they've ignored the righteousness God gives, wanting instead to be acceptable to God because of their own works, they've refused to submit to God's faith-righteousness.

Isaiah 64:6 (NKJ)

⁶But we are all like an unclean thing, and all our righteousnesses are like filthy rags; **(to God)** *We all fade as a leaf, and our iniquities, like the wind, have taken us away.*

Philippians 3:8-9 (NIV)

⁸What is more, I consider everything a loss because of the surpassing worth of knowing Christ Jesus my Lord, for Whose sake I have lost all things. I consider them garbage that I may gain Christ ⁹and be found in Him, not having a righteousness of my own that comes from the law, but that which is through faith in Christ—the righteousness that comes from God on the basis of faith.

B. **You can strive for perfection by diligently keeping the law without fail. You may think you're righteous, but you are _____.**

C. **Or you can _____ and receive Christ's righteousness by faith.**

1. No one has ever been declared righteous by the <u>works of the law</u>. It has always _____ to produce righteousness.

2. God said long ago, even before Christ died, that the righteous _____ by faith.

Answers: deceived, surrender, failed, live

82

3. It is not Christ plus works. What is it? Christ OR the law, blessing OR the curse, faith OR your works. _____ choose!

D. There were no curses for Abraham but only blessings because he _____ God.

Romans 4:3 (NIV)
³What does Scripture say? "Abraham believed God, and it was credited to him as righteousness."

Romans 4:5 (TPT)
⁵But no one earns God's righteousness. It can only be transferred when we no longer rely on our own works, but believe in the One Who powerfully declares the ungodly to be righteous in His eyes. It is faith that transfers God's righteousness into your account.

E. In the covenant with Abraham, God gave promises and blessings. He did not give an alternative to Abraham.

F. It produced a covenant of strong _____.

1. Abraham was _____ a friend.

James 2:23 (NIV)
²³And the scripture was fulfilled that says, "Abraham believed God, and it was credited to him as righteousness," and he was called God's friend.

Isaiah 41:8 (NIV)
⁸"But you, Israel, My servant, Jacob, whom I have chosen, you descendants of Abraham, My friend...

Answers: You, believed, friendship, called

2 Chronicles 20:7 (NIV)

7Our God, did You not drive out the inhabitants of this land before your people Israel and give it forever to the descendants of Abraham, Your friend?

2. This relationship is _____ in the Old Testament.

   a. Abraham is the _____ one who is called "The Friend of God".

   b. Praise God that in the New Covenant we are all called His_____.

John 15:14-15 (NIV)

14You are my friends if you do what I command. 15I no longer call you servants, because a servant does not know his master's business. Instead, I have called you friends, for everything that I learned from my Father I have made known to you.

Answers: unique, only, friends

A Blood Covenant that Can't Fail
Chapter 9

Point #1 Chapter 3 of Galatians Covers the Abrahamic Covenant

Galatians 3:13 (NIV)

¹³Christ redeemed us from the curse of the law by becoming a curse for us, for it is written: "Cursed is everyone who is hung on a pole."

Galatians 3:14 (TPT)

¹⁴Jesus, our Messiah, was cursed in our place and in so doing, dissolved the curse from our lives, so that all the blessings of Abraham can be poured out upon even non-Jewish believers.

A.　**The Gospel of Grace was _____ to Abraham.**

Galatians 3:8 (NKJ)

⁸And the Scripture, foreseeing that God would justify the Gentiles by faith, preached the gospel to Abraham beforehand, saying, "In you all the nations shall be blessed."

B.　**The covenant was between God and _____.**

Galatians 3:17 (TPT)

¹⁷This means that the covenant between God and Abraham was fulfilled in Messiah and cannot be altered.

Galatians 3:20 (TPT)

²⁰Now, a mediator does not represent just one party alone, but God fulfilled it all by Himself!

Answers: preached, Christ

Hebrews 6:13-14 (NKJ)

13For when God made a promise to Abraham, because He could swear by no one greater, He swore by Himself, 14saying, "Surely blessing I will bless you, and multiplying I will multiply you."

1. This was a _____ covenant.

2. The blood of Jesus Christ on the Mercy Seat of the Ark of the Covenant is a _____ of the Covenant God made between Himself and Jesus for us.

Point #2 God Enters Covenant with Abraham

Genesis 15:8-10 (NIV)

8But Abram said, "Sovereign LORD, how can I know that I will gain possession of it?" 9So the LORD said to him, "Bring me a heifer, a goat and a ram, each three years old, along with a dove and a young pigeon." 10Abram brought all these to him, cut them in two and arranged the halves opposite each other; the birds, however, he did not cut in half.

Genesis 15:12 (NIV)

12As the sun was setting, Abram fell into a deep sleep...

Genesis 15:17-18 (NIV)   WORD – JESUS – THE GROOM

17When the sun had set and darkness had fallen, <u>a smoking firepot</u> with a <u>blazing torch</u> appeared and <u>passed between the pieces.</u> 18On that day the LORD made a covenant with Abram...

Read Malachi 3:2-3 *Refiner's Fire*

Read Matthew 3:11 _____ *of Fire*

Red Jeremiah 23:29 *Word like* _____

Read Isaiah 30:27 *Tongue like a consuming Fire.*

Answers: blood, Baptism, Witness, Fire

86

Galatians 3:20 (TPT)
20Now, a mediator does not represent just one party alone, but God fulfilled it all by Himself!

Hebrews 6:13-14 (NKJ)
13For when God made a promise to Abraham, because He could swear by no one greater, He swore by Himself, 14saying, "Surely blessing I will bless you, and multiplying I will multiply you."

Point #3 The Old Covenant Between God and Man Couldn't Work

Galatians 3:22 (TPT)
22But the Scriptures make it clear that since we were all under the power of sin, we needed Jesus! And He is the Savior Who brings the promise to those who believe.

A. **Revelation of faith releases us from our good works (law) to the life of _____.**

    1.   Jesus is the Author, the Beginner, and the Starter of our _____.

what we do
⇩

Galatians 3:23 (TPT)
*23So until the revelation of faith for salvation was released, the **law** was a jailer, holding us as prisoners under lock and key until the "**faith**," which was destined to be revealed, would set us free.*
⇩

Whose faith? Jesus' faith.

    2.   The _____ of sin is the law.

Answers: grace, faith, power

3.   In and of ourselves, we have no _____ to set ourselves free from addictions, generational curses, etc. They run our lives.

4.   Law is what _____ do. It's our jailer. < It's the natural realm.>

    a.   <u>I'm</u> going to walk in love (what I do) _____ something happens that's not loving, and now, into jail I go!

    b.   <u>I'm</u> going to live in favor until _____ comes.

    c.   <u>I'm</u> going to live in joy until a storm comes.

    d.   <u>I'm</u> going to walk in wealth until _____ or lack comes.

    e.   <u>I'm</u> going to walk in health until sickness hits me, etc.

5.   Jesus already _____ it! Jesus already gave us:

    a.   Love
    b.   Favor
    c.   Joy
    d.   Wealth
    e.   Health and on and on…

Romans 3:24 (TPT)

[24]Yet through His powerful declaration of acquittal, God freely gives away His righteousness. His gift of love and favor now cascades over us, all because Jesus, the Anointed One, has liberated us from the guilt, punishment, and power of sin!

Answers: power, we, until, rejection, poverty, did

6.   The _____ led us to our life of grace.

Galatians 3:24 (TPT)
24The law becomes a gateway to lead us to the Messiah so that we would be saved by faith.

7.   _____ enters our hearts.

Galatians 3:25 (TPT)
25But when faith comes, the Law is no longer in force, since we have already entered into life.

8.   We belong to _____ now.

Galatians 3:29 (TPT)
29And since you've been united to Jesus, the Messiah, you are now Abraham's "child" and inherit all the promises of the Kingdom realm!

Point #4 Through Christ Jesus, we are now children of God.

Galatians 4:6 (TPT)
6And so that we would know for sure that we are His true children, God released the Spirit of Sonship into our hearts – moving us to cry out intimately, "My Father! You're our true Father!"

Genesis 12:2 (NIV)
2I will make you into a great nation, and I will bless you; I will make your name great, and you will be a blessing.

A.   You are an _____ of God.

Answers: law, Faith, Christ,   heir

Ephesians 3:14-15 (NIV)

[14]*For this reason I kneel before the Father,* [15]*from Whom every family in heaven and on earth derives its name.*

B.   Not our own name, but we wear His Name.

Elohim – _____

El Shaddai – Blessings

Adonai – In _____

Jehovah Jireh – Provision

Jehovah M'kaddesh – Holy

Jehovah Tsidkenu – Righteousness

Jehovah Nissi – _____

Jehovah Rophe – Healer

Jehovah Rohi – Shepherd

Jehovah _____ – Peace

Jehovah Shammah –Abiding

Ephesians 1:3 (TPT)

[3]*Every spiritual blessing in the heavenly realm has already been lavished upon us as a love gift from our wonderful heavenly Father, the Father of our Lord Jesus—all because He sees us wrapped into Christ. This is why we celebrate Him with all our hearts!*

Answers: Power, Charge, Victory, Shalom

C. God released the Spirit of Sonship into our _____ so we could receive God as our Father and confess it.

    1.   _____ God supernaturally fill the void of Fatherhood.

Hebrews 11:33 (TPT)
[33]Their faith fastened onto their promises and pulled them into reality!

    2.   That promise of son ship and receiving God as our Father needs to become a _____ to set us free from a wrong image of a father or lack of father.

Galatians 4:7 (TPT)
[7]Now we're no longer living like slaves under the law **(what we do)**, *but we enjoy being God's very own sons and daughters! And because we're His, we can access everything our Father has – for we are heirs of God through Jesus, the Messiah!*

    3.   You are loved because you _____.

Ephesians 5:1-2 (NIV)
[1]Follow God's example, therefore, as dearly loved children. [2]and walk in the way of love, just as Christ loved us and gave Himself up for us as a fragrant offering and sacrifice to God.

    4.   We love to provide for our children to set them up to win in life, but we expect them to bless and _____ us.

Ephesians 6:2 (NKJ)
[2]"Honor your father and mother," which is the first commandment with promise.

Answers: hearts, Let, reality, exist, praise

Proverbs 31:28 (NKJV)
28Her children rise up and call her blessed; her husband also, and he praises her.

1 John 3:1 (NIV)
1See what great love the Father has lavished on us, that we should be called children of God! And that is what we are!

Romans 8:16 (TPT)
16For the Holy Spirit makes God's Fatherhood real to us as He whispers into our innermost being, "You are God's beloved child!"

5.   Holy Spirit makes God's Fatherhood _____ to us.

D.   Love is not based on religious _____.

Romans 8:15 (TPT)
15And you did not receive the "spirit of religious duty," leading you back into the fear of never being good enough. But you have received the "Spirit of Full Acceptance," enfolding you into the family of God. And you will never feel orphaned, for as He rises up within us, our spirits join Him in saying the words of tender affection, "Beloved Father!"

Galatians 4:9 (TPT)
9But now that we truly know Him and understand how deeply we're loved by Him, why would we, even for a moment, consider turning back to those weak and feeble principles of religion, as though we were still subject to them?

Galatians 4:10 (TPT)
*10Why would we want to go backward into the bondage of religion – scrupulously observing **(extremely attentive)** rituals like special days, celebrations of the new moon, annual festivals, and sacred years?*

Answers: real, duty

Galatians 4:12 (TPT)

12Beloved ones, I plead with you, follow my example and become free from the bondage of religion.

E. Look at the contrast between law and grace.

1. The law makes you an _____. **Grace makes you a receiver.**

2. The law says, "DO." **Grace says, "Done."**

3. The law says, "_____to be holy." **Grace says, "You are holy."**

4. The law condemns. **Grace redeems.**

5. The law kills. **Grace gives _____.**

6. The law brings the curse. **Grace brings the _____.**

7. The law makes us sin conscious. **Grace makes us Christ conscious.**

8. The law was written on tablets of stone. **Grace is written on the tablets of our _____.**

9. The law brought bondage. **Grace brought freedom.**

10. Law is what you do. **Grace is what _____ has done.**

**Law is what you do.
Grace is what Christ has done.**

Answers: earner, Work, life, blessings, heart, Christ

93

Grace Brings Us into a Life of Love
Chapter 10

Point #1 The Two Covenants

A. Abraham had _____ sons.

Galatians 4:22-24 (NKJ)
22For it is written that Abraham had two sons: the one by a <u>bondwoman</u>, **(The bondwoman is symbolic of being a _____ to the curse such as addictions, sickness, poverty, rejection.)** *the other by a* <u>freewoman</u>. **(The freewoman is symbolic of the power and ability to set you free.)**
23But he who was of the bondwoman was born according to the flesh, and he of the freewoman through promise, 24 <u>which things are symbolic</u>. *For these are the two covenants: the one from Mount Sinai which gives birth to bondage, which is Hagar…*

> 1. The _____ realm has no power to change you.
>
> 2. The _____ realm of the New Covenant has the power to change you.

Galatians 4:24, 26 (TPT)
Old Covenant – Law - Slavery
24These two women and their sons express an allegory and become symbols of two covenants. The first covenant was born on Mt. Sinai **(law),** *birthing children into slavery – children born to Hagar.*

New Covenant – Supernatural – Freedom - Grace
26In contrast, there is a heavenly Jerusalem above us, which is our true "mother." She is the freewoman, birthing children into freedom!

Answers: two, slave, natural, supernatural

3. Ishmael's name means "_____."

4. Isaacs's name means "_____."

    a. Ishmael represents the ferocious wild activity of the _____. It's seeking to gain or earn God's love by what we do. It's a heavy yoke that only leads us to the curse.

    b. Isaac represents the _____ in the joy of knowing God has already done it for us and leads us to the blessings.

B. This is an outward picture of the Old Covenant (natural) and an inward _____ of the New Covenant (supernatural).

Genesis 21:8-10 (NKJ)
[8]*So the child grew and was weaned. And Abraham made a great feast on the same day that Isaac was weaned.* [9]*And Sarah saw the son of Hagar the Egyptian, whom she had borne to Abraham, scoffing.* [10]*Therefore she said to Abraham, "Cast out this bondwoman and her son; for the son of this bondwoman shall not be heir with my son, namely with Isaac."*

C. The picture of two covenants:

1. One covenant represents the natural. This is _____ who was conceived in the natural way.

2. The other covenant represents the supernatural of the Spirit. This is _____ who was conceived supernaturally.

Answers: wild, laughter, law, rest, working, Ishmael, Isaac

Galatians 4:28 (TPT)

²⁸Dear friend; just like Isaac, we're now the true children who inherit the Kingdom promises.

3.   We cannot _____ law and grace.

Galatians 4:29-30 (NKJ)

²⁹But, as he who was born according to the flesh **(the natural realm)** *then persecuted him who was born according to the Spirit,* ***(the supernatural realm)*** *even so it is now. ³⁰Nevertheless what does the Scripture say? "Cast out the bondwoman and her son, for the son of the bondwoman shall not be heir with the son of the freewoman."*

4.   The New Covenant is a covenant of the _____.

Galatians 4:31 (TPT)

It's now so obvious! We're not the children of the slave woman; we're the supernatural sons of the freewoman – sons of grace.

a.   The Old Covenant has no power to change you because it's on the outside.

b.   The New Covenant is on the _____ and has all of heaven's power to set you free. The New Covenant has the power to change you.

2 Corinthians 3:3 (NKJ)

³ clearly you are an epistle of Christ, ministered by us, written not with ink but by the Spirit of the living God, not on tablets of <u>stone</u> **(on the outside)** *but on tablets of* <u>flesh</u>, **(on the inside)** *that is, of the heart.*

5.   The Old Covenant _____. The New Covenant gives life.

Answers: mix, supernatural, inside, kills

96

2 Corinthians 3:6 (NKJ)

⁶Who also made us sufficient as ministers of the New Covenant, not of the letter but of the Spirit; for the letter kills, but the Spirit gives life.

6. The Old Covenant was a ministry of _____.

2 Corinthians 3:7 (NKJ)

⁷But if the ministry of death, written and engraved on stones...

7. The Old Covenant _____ and brings guilt, shame, and condemnation.

2 Corinthians 3:9 (NKJ)

⁹For if the ministry of condemnation had glory...

2 Corinthians 3:16-17 (NKJ)

¹⁶Nevertheless when one turns to the Lord, the veil is taken away. ¹⁷Now the Lord is the Spirit; and where the Spirit of the Lord is, there is liberty.

8. The New Covenant gives _____ from addictions, poverty, sickness, and rejection.

Point #2 Stand Fast in Your Freedom (Galatians, Chapter 5)

A. **Stand fast in your _____ that grace has given you.**

Galatians 5:1 (NIV)

¹It is for freedom that Christ has set us free.

Galatians 5:1 (NKJ)

¹Stand fast therefore in the liberty by which Christ has made us free, and do not be entangled again with a yoke of bondage.

Answers: death, condemns, freedom, freedom

Galatians 5:1 (TPT)

[1]Let me be clear, the Anointed One has set us free – not partially, but completely and wonderfully free! We must always cherish this truth and stubbornly refuse to go back into the bondage of our past.

B.   If you think you are made right by the law, you have _____ from grace.

Galatians 5:4 (NIV)

[4]You who are trying to be justified (**made right**) *by the law have been alienated* (**severed**) *from Christ; you have fallen away from grace.*

1.   Trying to be justified or made right by law, our works, will cause us to fall _____ from grace.

2.   In the revelation of grace, we see into the _____.

3.   The revelation of grace does not take place in the mind or intellect, but it comes by the Holy Spirit into our _____.

Luke 1:37 (TPT)

[37]Not one promise from God is empty of power, for nothing is impossible with God!

4.   The Covenant of Grace has the power to free us from _____ and bring us into the love for God and others.

Galatians 3:18 (NKJ)

[18]For if the inheritance is of the law, it is no longer of promise; but God gave it to Abraham by promise.

Answers: fallen, away, unseen, spirit, self

5. We get into self and out of love when we get under our own good _____.

6. The _____ can't get to us.

7. Without love, it's impossible for the blessings to get to us.

C. Faith works by love.

Galatians 5:6 (NKJV)
⁶For in Christ Jesus neither circumcision nor uncircumcision avails anything, but faith working through love.

1. Grace brings us into the love walk where faith is _____ by God's love.

Galatians 5:6b (TPT)
⁶All that matters now is living in the faith that is activated and brought to perfection by _____.

2. We are called to a _____ of freedom in the Holy Spirit.

Galatians 5:13 (TPT)
¹³Beloved ones, God has called us to live a life of freedom in the Holy Spirit. But don't view this wonderful freedom as an opportunity to set up a base of operations in the natural realm. Freedom means that we become so completely free of self-indulgence that we become servants of one another, expressing love in all we do.

Answers: works, blessings, activated, love, life

3.   Freedom means free of self-indulgence.

   a.   We are to _____ one another.

   b.   Love is an action; you _____ to love.
        Love is doing as in <u>The Five Love Languages</u>:

        1.   Words of Affirmation
        2.   Quality _____
        3.   Receiving Gifts
        4.   _____ of Service
        5.   Physical Touch

   c.   God's love completed the law of God. _____
        fulfilled the law.

Galatians 5:14 (TPT)
[14]For love completes the laws of God. All of the law can be summarized in one grand statement: "Demonstrate love to your neighbor, even as you care for and love yourself."

John 15:12 (NKJ)
[12] This is My commandment, that you love one another as I have loved you.

2 Corinthians 5:14 (NIV)
[4]For Christ's love compels us, because we are convinced that one died for all, and therefore all died.

Hebrews 6:10 (NIV)
[10]God is not unjust; He will not forget your work and the love you have shown Him as you have helped His people and continue to help them.

Answers: serve, decide, Time, Acts, Christ

d. Grace gives us loving _____.

Romans 7:4 (NKJ)
[4]*Therefore, my brethren, you also have become dead to the law through the body of Christ, that you may be married to another—to Him Who was raised from the dead, that we should bear fruit to God.*

2 Thessalonians 2:16-17 (NIV)
[16]*May our Lord Jesus Christ Himself and God our Father, Who loved us and by His grace gave us eternal encouragement and good hope,* [17]*encourage your hearts and strengthen you in every good deed and word.*

Colossians 4:6 (NIV)
[6]*Let your conversation be always full of grace, seasoned with salt, so that you may know how to answer everyone.*

Answers: words

Point #1 Grace Gives Us Loving Words

Galatians 5:15 (NIV)
15If you bite and devour each other, watch out or you will be destroyed by each other.

James 3:8 (NIV)
8but no human being can tame the tongue. It is a restless evil, full of deadly poison.

A.   The two-edged sword is the _____ of God.

Hebrews 4:12 (NKJ)
12For the Word of God is living and powerful, and sharper than any two-edged sword…

Hebrews 4:2 (TPT)
2…they didn't join their faith with the Word. Instead, what…they heard didn't affect them deeply, for they doubted.

>   1.   The Israelites did not join their faith with the Word of God and _____ its power.

Hebrews 4:12 (NKJ)
12For the Word of God is living and powerful, and sharper than any two-edged sword, piercing even to the division of soul and spirit, and of joints and marrow, and is a discerner of the thoughts and intents of the heart.

Answers: Word, activate

Hebrews 4:12 (AMP)
[12]For the Word of God is living and active and full of power [making it operative, energizing, and effective].

Ephesians 6:17 (NIV)
[17]Take ...the sword of the Spirit, which is the Word of God.

Revelation 1:16 (NIV)
[16]...and coming out of His **(Christ Jesus')** *mouth was a sharp, double-edged sword...*

Revelation 19:15 (NIV)
[15]Coming out of His mouth is a sharp sword with which to strike down the nations.

Mark 11:22-23 (NKJ)
[22]So Jesus answered and said to them, "Have faith in God. [23]For assuredly, I say to you, whoever says to this mountain, 'Be removed and be cast into the sea,' and does not doubt in his heart, but believes that those things he says will be done, he will have whatever he says."

B.   Faith as small as a mustard seed moves _____.

Matthew 17:20 (NKJ) (Jesus speaking)
[20]"...for assuredly I say to you, if you have faith as a mustard seed, you will say this mountain, 'Move from here to there,' and it will move; nothing will be impossible for you."

1.   Faith is like a hybrid _____ already. You cannot cross-breed it.

Answers: mountains, seed

C. Grace is powerful words.

Acts 20:32 (NIV)
32Now I commit you to God and to the word of His grace, which can build you up and give you an inheritance among all those who are sanctified.

2 Thessalonians 2:16-17 (NIV)
16May our Lord Jesus Christ Himself and God our Father, Who loved us and by His grace gave us eternal encouragement and good hope, 17encourage your hearts and strengthen you in every good deed and word.

1. Grace is _____ words.

2. Grace is words of success, _____, wealth, love, and faith.

Colossians 4:6 (NIV)
6Let your conversation be always full of grace, seasoned with salt, so that you may know how to answer everyone.

Hebrews 11:3 (TPT)
3Faith empowers us to see that the universe was created and beautifully coordinated by the power of God's words! He spoke and the invisible realm gave birth to all that is seen.

Point #2 Look at the Life of the Holy Spirit in Grace

Galatians 5:16 (NIV)
16So I say, walk by the Spirit, and you will not gratify **(fulfill, indulge, satisfy)** *the desires* **(appetite, addictions, cravings)** *of the flesh.* **<So strong in the natural that we need the power of grace.>**

Answers: supernatural, favor

A.   The _____ life is the life of the Holy Spirit.

Titus 2:11-12 (NIV)

*¹¹For the grace of God has appeared that offers salvation to all people. ¹² It **teaches us** to say "No" to ungodliness and worldly passions, and to live self-controlled, upright and godly lives in this present age.*

    1.   Grace _____ us:

        a.   Grace mentors us.
        b.   Grace _____ us.
        c.   It is the voice of the Holy Spirit.

Galatians 5:16 (TPT)

¹⁶As you yield freely and fully to the dynamic life and power of the Holy Spirit, you will abandon **(to give up completely)** *the cravings* **(urges, longings, wants)** *of your self-life.* **(compulsions of selfishness)**

B.   Your _____-life craves things that are against the Holy Spirit. The self-life cannot look beyond self to walk in God's love.

Galatians 5:17 (TPT)

¹⁷And the Holy Spirit's intense cravings **(wants)** *hinder your old self-life from dominating you! The Holy Spirit is the only One Who defeats the cravings of your natural life.*

    1.   The Holy Spirit _____ the cravings of the natural life.

Galatians 5:17 (TPT)

¹⁷The Holy Spirit is the only One Who defeats the cravings of your natural life.

Answers: grace, teaches, trains, self, defeats

105

2. We have full _____ of the Spirit of Grace.

Galatians 5:18 (TPT)
18But when you are brought into the full freedom of the Spirit of Grace, you will no longer be living under the domination of the law, but soaring above it!

3. The acts of the self-life are _____.

Galatians 5:19-21 (TPT)
19The cravings of the self-life are obvious: sexual immorality, lustful thoughts, pornography, 20chasing after things instead of God, manipulating others, hatred of those who get in your way, senseless arguments, resentment when others are favored, temper tantrums, angry quarrels, only thinking of yourself, being in love with your own opinions, 21being envious of the blessings of others, murder, uncontrolled addictions, wild parties, and all other similar behavior.

C. The fruit of the Holy Spirit has many _____.

Galatians 5:22 (TPT)
2But the fruit produced by the Holy Spirit within you is divine love in all its various expressions: **(many facets)**

1. We have every opportunity, all day, to give God's divine love, in all its expressions, to those who are in need.

Galatians 5:22-23 (TPT)
23Joy that _____, peace that subdues, patience that endures, _____ in action, a life full of virtue, **(high moral_____)** *faith that prevails,* **(wins)** *gentleness of heart, and strength of spirit. Never set the law above these qualities, for they are meant to be _____.*

Answers: freedom, obvious, facets, overflows, kindness, standards, limitless

106

2.   These qualities are limitless.

Galatians 5:22-23 (NIV)

²²But the fruit of the Spirit is love, joy, peace, forbearance, kindness, goodness, faithfulness, ²³gentleness and <u>self-control</u>. Against such things there is no law. **(In grace, there is no law.)**

    a.   The word "self" is not found in *self-control*; the word is actually lordship control or _____ control. (Spirit is in control.)

3.   The fruit of the Holy Spirit is meant to be limitless.

D.   In the life of grace, we _____ the sinful nature.

Galatians 5:24 (NIV)

²⁴Those who belong to Christ Jesus have crucified the flesh **(Godless human nature <sin, _____ of Godless nature>)** *with its passions and desires.* **(appetites)**

<u>Point #3 The grace life is a life surrendered to the freedom of the Holy Spirit.</u>

Galatians 5:25 (TPT)

²⁵We must _____ in the Holy Spirit and follow after Him.

A.   We are never arrogant or look down on others.

Galatians 5:26 (TPT)

²⁶So may we never be arrogant, or look down on another, for each of us is an original. We must forsake all jealousy that diminishes the value of others.

Answers: Spirit, crucify, emotions, live

1.   Never be found dishonoring another.

2.   We don't compare ourselves to each other; we are each one of a kind, _____.

3.   We _____ all jealousy that diminishes the value of others.

Answers: unique, forsake

108

Grace Shows Mercy
Chapter 12

Grace Makes You a _____; Law Makes You an Earner

Grace is Others First; Law is _____-First

Grace is _____-Powered; Law is Self-Powered

Grace is What Christ Has _____; Law is What You Do

Grace _____ You; Law Condemns

Grace Makes You _____-Conscious;
Law makes You Sin-Conscious

When Self Dies, Grace Lives

Self and Law are _____Meanings

Grace and Christ are Like Meanings

The Law was given for the _____ to civilize it.

Grace was given to the <u>Redeemed</u>
because no one is capable of keeping the whole Law.

In this chapter of the book, we are looking at what Paul is saying
to us of the behavior in the Kingdom of God in grace.

Answers: Receiver, Self, God, Done, Qualifies, Christ, Like, world

Point #1 What our behavior should be toward the weaker person.

A. _____ him or her.

Galatians 6:1 (TPT)
[1]My beloved friends, if you see a believer who is overtaken with a fault, may the one who overflows with the Spirit seek to <u>restore</u> him. Win him over with gentle words, which will open his heart to you and will keep you from exalting yourself over him.

1. The Greek word for <u>restore</u> here means <u>to reset as a dislocated bone.</u>

   a. This is a medical term. This verb is in the present action which says, "It might take some _____."

   b. So don't get discouraged if it doesn't happen overnight.

2. People sometimes make bad _____, have financial problems, relationship problems, accusations made against them, experience sickness, or they lost their job.

3. People are in torment and bound by addictions, relapse, alcohol, drugs, sexual sins, etc.

B. **Who is to do the restoring? Those who are controlled by the** _____.

Galatians 6:1 (TPT) ⌐ **fruit of the Spirit-Holy Spirit words**
*[1]Win him over with **<u>gentle words</u>**, which will open his heart to you and will keep you from exalting yourself over him.*

Answers: Restore, time, decisions, Spirit

Ephesians 1:8 (TPT)

⁸This superabundant grace is already powerfully working in us and flooding into every part of our being, releasing within us all forms of wisdom and practical understanding.

1. How was Jesus with people?

    a. He _____ the sick.

    b. He opened blind eyes.

    c. He forgave and set free the _____ caught in adultery.

    d. He ministered to the woman at the well who had five husbands.

2. How are legalistic people with people?

    a. Legalist people _____ people.

    b. Legalistic people put shame on people.

    c. Legalistic people put _____ on people.

3. You are not to complain about the weak person, gossip about them, or run them out of the fellowship.

    a. That person is to be put back _____ into the right place in the Body.

Answers: healed, woman, condemn, guilt, gently

111

b.   Put back in the Body gently, because he/she is as _____ as a dislocated bone, and it hurts to be treated roughly.

4.   A dislocated bone may take some time to function correctly again.

   a.   A weaker person must be given some time to _____ strong and slowly begin to take on the responsibilities that belong to them.

5.   Ephesians 5:20 says, *"...we are members of His body"*.

   a.   Just as members of your body take care of each other, sheltering and protecting the _____ parts.

   b.   We help the members of Christ's Body that are temporarily "dislocated," and get them back into place.

   c.   _____ them until they are strong again.

6.   The legalistic person would condemn this person, but the spiritual person will _____ them.

7.   _____ shoots the wound or kicks the wounded when they are down, condemns, shames, and makes them feel guilty.

8.   To sum it up, let all be loving, merciful, brotherly, kind-hearted, and humble in spirit toward them.

Answers: tender, grow, hurting, Protect, restore, Religion

a. Use good, loving, and kind words full of hope and a better _____.

9. They need to know that God's purpose for them will stand!

Isaiah 46:10 (NIV)
[10]I make known the end from the beginning, from ancient times, what is still to come. I say, "My purpose will stand, and I will do all that I please."

10. They need to know _____ already did it for them.

Romans 4:7-8 (AMPC)
[7]Blessed and happy and to be envied are those whose iniquities are forgiven and whose sins are covered up and completely buried. [8]Blessed and happy and to be envied is the person of whose sin the Lord will take no account nor reckon it against him.

Romans 8:28 (NIV)
[28]And we know that in all things God works for the good of those who love Him, who have been called according to His purpose.

C. Our behavior toward the weaker person should be: Stay out of pride and get into the supernatural _____ of God.

Galatians 6:1 (TPT)
Win him over with gentle words **(hope, encouragement, love)**, *which will open his heart to you and will keep you from exalting yourself over Him.* **(grace)**

1. Never _____ the power of grace.

Answers: tomorrow, God, power, doubt

113

2. God's grace fuels your passion.

James 4:6 (NIV84)
6God opposes the proud, but gives grace to the humble.

3. You know it's Christ in you.

4. The law _____ the person.

5. Grace _____the person.

6. God calls us to love.

John 13:34 (NIV)
34A new command I give you: Love one another. As I have loved you, so you must love one another.

Colossians 1:27 (NIV)
27To them God has chosen to make known among the Gentiles the glorious riches of this mystery, which is Christ in you, the hope of glory.

7. You, as the spiritual one, may restore the brother or sister with _____, but you do it only as a result of the grace of God. <What Christ has done.>

    a. The Sword of the Spirit is in your mouth.

    b. Grace gives you _____ to speak. You can't tame your tongue.

Answers: condemns, restores, gentleness, words

James 3:8 (NIV)
⁸but no human being can tame the tongue. It is a restless evil, full of deadly poison.

Hebrews 4:12 (NIV)
¹²For the Word of God is alive and active. Sharper than any double-edged sword, it penetrates even to dividing soul and spirit, joints and marrow; it judges the thoughts and attitudes of the heart.

Revelation 1:16 (NIV)
¹⁶In His right hand He held seven stars, and coming out of His mouth was a sharp, double-edged sword. His face was like the sun shining in all its brilliance.

8.   The Holy Spirit is the Helper.

    a.   The Holy Spirit helps us to trust and _____ on Christ all the more.

    b.   Helping another brother or sister should never be cause for us to lift ourselves in _____.

    c.   We _____ ourselves to the mercy of God and God's compassion and love.

I Corinthians 13:4-5 (TPT)
⁴Love is large and incredibly patient. Love is gentle and consistently kind to all. It refuses to be jealous when blessing comes to someone else. Love does not brag about one's achievements nor inflate its own importance. ⁵Love does not traffic in shame...

Answers: lean, pride, bind

9.   Love is _____ and incredibly patient.

10. Love is gentle and _____ kind to all.

    a.   How was Jesus with the demon-possessed man who was filled and tormented by a legion of demons? Jesus didn't condemn, shame or judge him (a man that caused the city much harm), but Jesus restored him with love and compassion.

    b.   This is how grace should _____ in our lives.

11. Love does not traffic in shame.

Luke 8:27-36 (NIV)

[27]*When Jesus stepped ashore, He was met by a demon-possessed man from the town. For a long time this man had not worn clothes or lived in a house, but had lived in the tombs.* [28]*When he saw Jesus, he cried out and fell at His feet, shouting at the top of his voice,*

"What do you want with me, Jesus, Son of the Most High God? I beg you, don't torture me!" [29]*For Jesus had commanded the impure spirit to come out of the man. Many times it had seized him, and though he was chained hand and foot and kept under guard, he had broken his chains and had been driven by the demon into solitary places.* [30]*Jesus asked him,*

"What is your name?"

"Legion," he replied, because many demons had gone into him. [31]*And they begged Jesus repeatedly not to order them to go into the Abyss.* [32]*A large herd of pigs was feeding there on the hillside. The demons begged Jesus to let them go into the pigs, and He gave them permission* [33]*When the demons came out of the man, they went into the pigs, and*

Answers: large, consistently, look

the herd rushed down the steep bank into the lake and was drowned.
³⁴When those tending the pigs saw what had happened, they ran off and
reported this in the town and countryside, ³⁵and the people went out to
see what had happened. When they came to Jesus, they found the man
from whom the demons had gone out, sitting at Jesus' feet, dressed and
in his right mind; and they were afraid. ³⁶Those who had seen it told
the people how the demon-possessed man had been cured.

Point #2 What our behavior should be toward brothers or sisters in trouble.

A.   We are to carry their _____.

Galatians 6:2 (TPT)
²Love empower us **(gives us that supernatural extra power)** *to fulfill*
the law **(love)** *of the Anointed One as we carry each other's troubles.*

    1.   The law of the Anointed One, Christ Jesus, in the New
        Covenant is _____.

    2.   The legalists in Jesus' day did the _____
        of restoring. They added heavy burdens upon the people by
        imposing the law upon the new believer.

    3.   The legalists used the moments when people were down to
        abuse, _____, and condemn them. They used
        guilt and they even stoned them to death.

Matthew 23:4 (NIV)
⁴They tie up heavy, cumbersome loads and put them on other people's
shoulders, but they themselves are not willing to lift a finger to move
them.

Answers: troubles, love, opposite, shame

117

4.   Many times it's just the _____ we say or how we say it.

5.   Peter interceded on behalf of the early Gentile Christians. He asked the Jewish (Christian) leaders not to put heavy burdens on the _____ believers.

Acts 15:10 (NIV)
[10]Now then, why do you try to test God by putting on the necks of Gentiles a yoke that neither we nor our ancestors have been able to bear?

Ephesians 3:20 (TPT)
[20]Never doubt God's mighty power to work in you and accomplish all this. He will achieve infinitely more than your greatest request, your most unbelievable dream, and exceed your wildest imagination! He will outdo them all, for His miraculous power constantly energizes you.

6.   Jesus said,

Matthew 11:28 (TAB)
[28]Come to Me, all you who labor and are heavy-laden and over burdened, and I will cause you to rest – I will ease and relieve and refresh your souls.

a.   Jesus says, "I did it all! Enter My _____. Take My yoke" <My works on> meaning, "I've already done it!"

B.   It is _____ will for His people to have help with their burdens when they are in a tragedy, crisis or relapse.

Answers: words, new, rest, God's

Romans 15:1-2 (NIV)

[1]We who are strong ought to bear with the <u>failings</u> of the weak and not to please ourselves. [2]Each of us should please our neighbors for their good, to <u>build them up</u>. **<to empower them>**

1. What are _____ going to do with the troubles of another person?

   a. *Failings* is burdens *"<u>barros</u>"* the Greek word for *"<u>a very heavy weight,</u>"* anything _____ on one physically.

2. Troubles in life make a _____ on one's resources, whether material, spiritual or religious.

   a. Can you depend upon yourself to be strong enough to carry another's trouble or burden? <u>I don't think so!</u>

3. The only reason the Lord asks you to help carry another's troubles is to give them over to the <u>Great Trouble Carrier,</u> _____!

Psalm 55:22 (NIV)

[22]Cast your cares on the Lord, and He will sustain you; He will never let the righteous be shaken. **<Measureless grace will strengthen you.>**

I Peter 5:7 (NIV)

[7]...cast all your anxiety on Him, because He cares for you.

Answers: you, pressing, demand, Jesus

119

4.   Sometimes a brother or sister is so taken up with the weight of his or her burden that he or she

    a.   Has been_____.

    b.   They are _____ to get the burden rolled over to the Lord.

5.   Help them!

    a.   This may mean _____ for deliverance.

    b.   Reading the Word to him or her.

    c.   It may mean _____ their children for a day while he or she attends a conference to be refreshed.

    d.   Whatever it takes, do it!

6.   But don't come away carrying his or her burden. It is to be _____ upon the Lord!

C.   To fulfill the Law of Christ is to love as Jesus has loved us.

1.   We have already seen what the law of _____ is.

John 13:34 (NIV)
34A new command I give you: Love one another. As I have loved you, so you must love one another.

2.   The Law of Christ is loving our neighbor.

Answers: weakened, unable, praying, babysitting, cast, Christ

a. When we show as much concern over the burdens of our neighbor as we do for our own burdens, then we will be _____ them.

b. _____ love and mercy to them and do everything possible to get rid of that burden.

c. Then show your brother or sister _____ to deal victoriously with others who are trying to overcome them.

Point #3 What Our Behavior Should be Toward Ourselves

Ephesians 1:11 (TPT)
[11]Before we were even born, He gave us our destiny; that we would fulfill the plan of God Who always accomplishes every purpose and plan in His heart.

A. The Covenant of Grace is what Christ has done. It's a supernatural life.

Galatians 6:3 (NIV)
[3]If anyone thinks they are something when they are not, they deceive themselves.

B. _____ yourself.

2 Corinthians 13:5 (NIV)
[5]Examine yourselves to see whether you are in the faith; test yourselves. Do you not realize that Christ Jesus is in you—unless, of course, you fail the test?

Answers: bearing, Demonstrate, how, Examine

1. You are nothing of yourself.

    a. Your _____ wisdom is nothing.

1 Corinthians 3:18-20 (NIV)

[18]*Do not deceive yourselves. If any of you think you are wise by the standards of this age, you should become "fools" so that you may become wise.* [19]*For the wisdom of this world is foolishness in God's sight. As it is written: "He catches the wise in their craftiness";* [20]*and again, "The Lord knows that the thoughts of the wise are futile."*

Ephesians 1:8 (TPT)

[8]*This superabundant grace is already powerfully working in us, releasing within us all forms of wisdom and practical understanding.*

    b. _____ can do nothing of yourself.

John 15:5 (NIV)

[5]*I am the vine; you are the branches. If you remain in Me and I in you, you will bear much fruit; apart from Me you can do nothing.*

2. Do not _____ yourself.

Galatians 6:3 (NKJV)

[3]*For if anyone thinks himself to be something, when he is nothing, he deceives himself.*

    a. The deception that Paul is talking about here is that of _____ -importance without Christ.

    b. There is the _____ to think, "I'm so great, of course I can help him; let me at him."

Answers: own, You, deceive, self, temptation

122

c. That is a deception because without Christ "you can do nothing."

d. When we are weak, we say we are strong, but the only reason we can do that is because, "I can do all things through _____ Who strengthens me."

e. The believer who is most spiritual is utterly dependent upon God Who is the strongest.

3. Your adequacy comes from _____. In the Covenant of Grace, it's what Christ has already done.

2 Corinthians 3:4-6 (NIV)
⁴Such confidence we have through Christ before God. ⁵Not that we are competent in ourselves to claim anything for ourselves, but our competence comes from God. ⁶He has made us competent as ministers of a new covenant—not of the letter but of the Spirit; for the letter kills, but the Spirit gives life.

Philippians 4:13 (NIV)
¹³I can do all this through Him Who gives me strength.

Philippians 4:13 (TPT)
¹³And I find that the strength in Christ's explosive power infuses me to conquer every difficulty.

C. Examine your own _____.

1. We are not _____ our own work with another's.

Answers: Christ, God, work, comparing

Galatians 6:4 (TPT)

[4]*Let everyone be devoted to fulfill the work God has given them to do with excellence, and their joy will be in doing what's right and being themselves and not in being affirmed by others.*

2 Corinthians 10:12 (TPT)

[12]*Of course we wouldn't dare to put ourselves in the same class or compare ourselves with those who rate themselves so highly. They compare themselves to one another and make up their own standards to measure themselves by, and then they judge themselves by their own standards. What self-delusion!*

Galatians 5:26 (TPT)

[26]*So may we never be found arrogant, or look down on another, for each of us is an original.*

Point #4 Bear your own load and run your own race in Christ Jesus.

A.   Bear your _____ load.

Galatians 6:5 (NKJ)

[5]*For each one shall bear his own load.*

1.   The word *load* is not the heavy burden of verse two. In Greek it is "*phortion*" or "something to be carried" (This means our responsibilities, our obligations, and our _____).

   a.   It is the same word that was used with carrying a soldier's _____. A soldier carries his own pack and does not expect another to carry it. Each bears the responsibility for his own pack.

Answers: own, calling, pack

124

B. Run your own _____.

   1.   These are your responsibilities.

      a.   Your _____ is your responsibility.

      b.   Your ministry and your job are your responsibilities.

      c.   The neighbor that is _____ is your responsibility.

   2.   Walk in love.

   3.   You must carry your own " _____ pack" in order to effectively carry out the orders of your Commander -in-Chief, Christ Jesus!

   4.   Everyone must do his own work!

C. We each have a race to run that has already been _____ by Christ.

   1.   The self-centered person wants you to _____ their race.

      a.   They need to pick up their responsibilities.

      b.   They want _____ to carry their load – expect it.

      c.   They don't want to get well.

      d.   They want to be taken _____ of.

Answers: race, family, lost, soldier's, fulfilled, run, you, care

e.   They have a total addiction to _____.

f.   They expect this of the Christian and the church; they are thieves and _____ in life.

g.   They are consumed with self.

Grace is a Life of Giving
Chapter 13

Point #1 What behavior should we have toward our teachers?

A. _____ all good things.

Galatians 6:6 (AMP)
⁶The one who is taught the Word [of God] is to share all good things with his teacher [contributing to his spiritual and material support].

1. It is scriptural to pay wages and share material _____ with those who teach you the Word.

I Corinthians 9:10, 11, 14 (NIV)
¹⁰Surely He says this for us, doesn't He? Yes, this was written for us, because whoever plows and threshes should be able to do so in the hope of sharing in the harvest. ¹¹If we have sown spiritual seed among you, is it too much if we reap a material harvest from you? ¹⁴In the same way, the Lord has commanded that those who preach the gospel should receive their living from the gospel.

2. One seed planted in the natural creates _____ of seeds.

3. One seed planted in the Kingdom of God creates super-natural multiplication of seed.

4. Give your way out of _____.

Answers: Share, blessings, thousands, poverty

Philippians 4:17, 19 (MSG)

17Not that I'm looking for handouts, but I do want you to experience the blessing that issues from generosity. 19...pleasing God no end. You can be sure that God will take care of everything you need, His generosity exceeding even yours in the glory that pours from Jesus.

Philippians 4:19 (NKJ)

19And my God shall supply all your need according to His riches in glory by Christ Jesus.

B.   Giving and being generous causes you to _____ a harvest.

C.   We give out of our _____.

Galatians 6:7 (TPT)

7Make no mistake about it, God will never be mocked! For what you plant will always be the very thing you harvest.

Galatians 6:7 (AMP)

7... for whatever a man sows, this and this only is what he will reap.

1.   In order for a farmer to reap a crop of wheat, he must first _____ seed by sowing it in the ground. Then, and only then, can he rightfully expect to reap a harvest.

2.   Many people want to do a lot of reaping but never do any sowing. God gave us the _____ here to take care of our teachers.

   a.   The _____ was not just to meet the physical needs of the spiritual leaders.

Answers: reap, need, plant, plan, purpose

1. God wanted to give you a way to reap a _____ harvest.

2. God wanted an _____ of blessing for you. That is the reason you are to share your goods.

2 Corinthians 9:6 (NIV)
⁶Remember this: Whoever sows sparingly will also reap sparingly, and whoever sows generously will also reap generously.

2 Corinthians 9:6 (AMPC)
⁶ [Remember] this: he who sows sparingly and grudgingly will also reap sparingly and grudgingly, and he who sows generously [that blessings may come to someone] will also reap generously and with blessings.

3. When we sow generously we reap _____.

4. We reap _____ much!

5. We reap abundance, even superabundance.

6. We reap inexhaustible _____.

Proverbs 11:24-25 (NIV)
²⁴One person gives freely, yet gains even more; another withholds unduly, but comes to poverty. ²⁵A generous person will prosper.

D. Examine your _____.

1. You reap what you sow!

Answers: big, avenue, generously, too, blessings, seed

129

a. That is, if you sow good seed, you will reap a harvest of _____ of blessings.

b. This principle can apply to you.

1. Plant what you _____ to harvest!

2. _____ seeds will produce corruption or weeds.

3. _____ seeds will produce eternal life and increase of blessings.

Galatians 6:8 (MSG)

[8]*The person who plants selfishness, ignoring the needs of others— ignoring God!—harvests a crop of weeds. All he'll have to show for his life is weeds!*

E. Examine the _____.

1. Sowing to yourself is not productive.

2. Sowing to yourself will produce the negative in your life or _____.

a. It is possible to spend most of your material goods on yourself, on your own pleasures. That is not good soil; you will reap weeds.

b. Sowing to self will _____ out the blessings.

Answers: increase, expect, Carnal, Supernatural, soil, weeds, choke

F.   Who gets to have the crop?

1.   The one who _____ is the one who reaps an increase of blessings.

2.   Always be sure that you are sowing in _____ soil, and you will be blessed with the harvest!

G.   Be patient. Crops take_____ to grow.

Galatians 6:9 (TPT)
⁹And don't allow yourselves to be weary or disheartened in planting good seeds, for the season of reaping the wonderful harvest you've planted is coming!

1.   God's promise ensures that we will _____.

   a.   He warns us about growing weary.

2.   After you have planted seed, there is a growing _____ before harvest.

   a.   Many people are impatient and want to go out the next day and reap a huge harvest.

   b.   When there is nothing, they become angry and say, "It doesn't work, I may as well _____ sowing."

      1.   That is the wrong attitude.

   c.   We need to be planting _____ for what we need next year.

Answers: sows, good, time, reap, time, quit, today

1.   Constant planting ensures _____ reaping.

3.   God's crops always come in.

PRAYER OF SALVATION

Salvation does not mean following a bunch of rules to try to keep God happy. The truth is that He loves you and wants you to experience joy, health, peace and prosperity. You can only do that knowing Jesus as a Friend and Savior.

How can you be saved? It is a matter of simply believing. The Bible says: If you confess with your mouth the Lord Jesus and believe in your heart that God has raised Him from the dead, you will be saved. (Romans 10:9)

If you believe, then pray this prayer:
"Dear Father God, I ask you to forgive me of all my sins. Jesus, come into my heart, come into my life, be my Lord and Savior. In Jesus name, Amen. Jesus is Lord!"

Congratulations! You made the very best decision you have ever made or ever will make. Now you are saved. You are forgiven and you are on your way to heaven. The next step is to grow in this new relationship with God. The best way to do that is to read your Bible every day so that God can speak to you through it, and get involved in a good church so that you can have support and fellowship with other believers.

We would love to hear from you!
If you received Christ as your personal Savior, we want to send you a free Bible. Email us at thewordforwinners@gmail.com or visit us online at Thewordforwinners.com

MORE BOOKS BY THE ANDERSONS

Dr. Maureen Anderson (See thewordforwinners.com)

God's Grace Fuels My Passion
Releasing the Miraculous Through Fasting with Prayer
Are You Spirit Led or Emotionally Driven
Damaged DNA
Making Impossibilities Possible
Confessing God's Word (Leather Bound)
Releasing Miracles by Speaking God's Word
How to Hear from the Holy Spirit
Will the Real Me Please Stand Up?

Drs. C. Thomas and Maureen Anderson

Marriage Beyond the Dream
Name of the Game-Victim, Enabler, Persecutor, Helper
Health God's Way
Building a Flourishing Church God's Way

Dr. C. Thomas Anderson (See drcthomasanderson.org)

Becoming a Millionaire God's Way Part 1
Becoming a Millionaire God's Way Workbook
Too Much Money
Will the Real America Please Stand Up?
No More Sacred Cows, Grace > Religion
LOL Your Way to Life – Anecdotes and One-Liners to Get You through Your Day
Releasing the Blessings You Can't Contain
Personal Growth to Power – Jesus Between the Lines-18 Power Principles to Success
The Big Six of Genesis
Grace Carved in Wood
Mind Over What Matters
The Money System – Are You Being Dumbed Down?
The Essence of Creation – 7 Principles
PLEASE Train Up Your Child – Character Determines Your Child's Destiny
Where the Blessings Are
My God is Only Good
Jesus Wasn't Poor
10 Principles for a Good Life from a Good God

INVITE DR. MAUREEN ANDERSON TO SPEAK!

If you desire to have Dr. Maureen Anderson speak at your event or church, please call 1-480-669-0102 or visit our website, **thewordforwinners.com** and fill out the invite form or email maureen@thewordforwinners.com

Join The Word for Winners Family today!

Yes, I want to join Maureen Anderson in partnership. Enclosed is my first offering of $ _____ to establish my monthly partnership and help reach the world with the Word of Grace.

_____ Please contact me to show me how to receive my free e-book for becoming a monthly partner.

Name _____
Address _____
City _____
State _____ Zip _____
Phone (_____) _____
Email _____

_____ I would like to set up an automatic gift from my debit or credit card.
_____ I would like to donate one time today.

Card Number _____ Code _____
Expiration Date _____
Name on the Card _____

Send to: The Word for Winners
             P.O. Box 22229
             Mesa, AZ 85277

I sow this seed in faith believing that God will meet my
need:_____
_____

Thank You!
If you would like prayer, call the prayer line, 480-669-0102.
www.thewordforwinners.com

135

Made in the USA
Monee, IL
10 October 2023